Flowers of Field and Forest

Flowers of

THE MACMILLAN COMPANY · NEW YORK

Field and Forest

CLARENCE J. HYLANDER

Illustrated by the author

COLLIER-MACMILLAN LIMITED · LONDON

29110

The Macmillan Company, New York
Collier-Macmillan Canada, Ltd., Toronto, Ontario
Library of Congress catalog card number: 62-9279
Printed in the United States of America
Second Printing 1966

FOREWORD

Flowers of Field and Forest is the story of our wild flowers in their home surroundings. Plants have homes, in the sense of a definite place to live, as much as animals do. Wild flowers do not grow and thrive in a hit-or-miss fashion wherever a seed happens to fall. Every kind of plant inherits a certain type of structure and habits suited for certain living conditions: bright sunlight or shade, dry or humid air, high or low temperatures, water-soaked or parched soil, north or south hillsides. Thus the place in which daisies or cattails live provides the special combination of surroundings—known as the environment—for which each of these plants is particularly suited.

You would never think of looking up someone in a strange town without knowing his address. The habitat, or special environment, of a wild flower is its address; when you know this, you have some idea where to look

v

for it. The type of home preferred by a wild flower provides a valuable clue as to what kinds will be found on a dry roadside bank, a swampy meadow, or a forest glade. Usually several kinds of wild flowers are adapted for living in the same habitat. These become a neighborhood with the same local address, a wild-flower community. As a result, wherever we find a flower, we can expect to find also other species which require the same living conditions.

Thus *Flowers of Field and Forest* is not merely a guide to the identification of wild flowers. It has as its aim, in addition, getting acquainted with plant communities and the special living conditions found in each. Biologists call this the ecological approach, for ecology is the study of organisms in relation to their environment. At the same time we will identify the typical wild flowers of each community, relying on sets of clues that can assist us in recognizing individual species.

Flowers of Field and Forest has a broad scope, describing the wild-flower communities you can expect to find in New England and the prairie states as well as in Florida and California. With such a goal it is impossible within the limits of this book to introduce you to every kind of flower you may meet. The subject matter is restricted to herbaceous plants with conspicuous flowers, thus eliminating woody vines and shrubs as well as grasses. Even excluding these, the wild-flower population of the United States and Canada includes a tremendous number of species. In the northeastern United States, for example, there are over 3,000 different kinds of wild flowers. A complete list of those found in the southeastern United States would include over 4,000 species. In southern California alone the plant communities include some 2,000 wild flowers. Thus it is obvious that the 200 species selected for this book form only a small, though representative, proportion of the total wild-flower population.

A most significant factor in a plant's environment is the available water supply. Plants vary greatly in their demands for water. Some tolerate and even require considerable water, others get along on very little, and many others prefer the various gradations of soil moisture between these extremes. We begin our exploration of wild-flower communities (Chapter Three) with those that have their homes in streams, ponds, and lakes; such aquatic habitats are most abundant in the eastern and southeastern United States. Then we visit (Chapter Four) the less aquatic but yet wet habitats of swamps, bogs, moist woods, and fields. These habitats are also most abundant in the eastern half of the United States, especially along the Atlantic coastal plain. As our explorations lead us to higher and relatively drier ground we become familiar with the wild flowers of moderately moist, shaded habitats of woods and forests (Chapter Five). These living conditions occur in the forested eastern and far western portions of the United States, and are relatively rare in the central prairie states. Finally we explore the much drier, sunnier habitats of fields and roadsides (Chapter Six) where wild flowers live which can get along in sandy, poor soil or under extreme conditions of bright sunlight and little rainfall. Such habitats occur in all our states, but are particularly abundant in the central states and in the Southwest.

As in the other titles in the *Young Naturalist Series* *
we have added in the *Afterword* some suggestions for
flower books that you will find valuable in a more detailed
identification of wild flowers and a useful addition to your
nature library. In the *Index and Guide to Classification*
you will find the common and scientific names of the species described in this book, arranged according to families
and the classification scheme used by botanists.

An enjoyment of the out-of-doors depends upon how
much you observe, and how well you understand what you
see. To be able to call a flower by its correct name is a
satisfying achievement. But it becomes even more satisfying when you recognize the flower as a living thing with
"likes" and "dislikes," and have learned why it is able to
live where and how it does. I hope that *Flowers of Field
and Forest* will give you a dynamic viewpoint of plant
life; and understanding of the close relationship between
a wild flower and its environment, as well as a compre-
hensive view of the plant community of which it is a part.

Clarence J. Hylander
Bar Harbor, Maine
January, 1962

* *Sea and Shore, Trees and Trails, Animals in Armor, Insects
on Parade, Animals in Fur, Feathers and Flight* are six previous
titles in this series; they present an elementary excursion into the
biology of marine life, trees, reptiles, insects, mammals, and birds.

CONTENTS

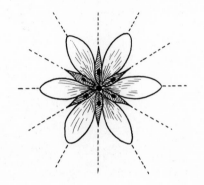

Swampy ponds provide an ideal home for communities of such typical hydrophytes as cattails and pond lilies.

CHAPTER ONE

HOW THE HOMES
OF WILD FLOWERS DIFFER

As one explores the woods and fields, he cannot fail to notice that flowers grow in many different types of places, each location offering living conditions which differ from those of other sites. He will also notice that the same kind of flower seems to grow always in the same sort of surroundings. Bladderwort and water lily make their homes in ponds. Skunk cabbage and forget-me-not establish themselves along the marshy borders of streams. Orchid and trillium prefer rich shaded woods while columbine grows on the rocky sides of ravines. Daisy, lupine, and owl's clover spread over acres of sunny fields. The cactus flourishes in inhospitable deserts. This distribution of wild flowers, each with a preference for where it lives, reveals the close relationship that exists between the structure and habits of a plant, and the living conditions of its chosen home.

Plants and Their Environment

Every species of wild flower has distinctive characteristics by which it can be recognized. In many cases these characteristics are adaptations to a particular way of life. Some plants, such as the lady's slipper, have large thin leaves, others have small thick ones like the mayflower's. Some leaves are smooth and shiny, like those of trillium; others are rough or bristly like mullein and hawkweed. Some kinds of violets are stemless, other plants, like water parsnip have tall branching stems. Cacti and other desert plants have deep-penetrating root systems; buttercups and violets have shallow roots. Differences are found also in the flowers, with their variety of color and scent, their simplicity or complexity of structure, their various methods of pollination, their different types of fruits and seeds.

If we shift our attention to the environment we discover that this, too, is far from uniform. In a large region such as the United States, the land provides topographic variety which sets the stage for many kinds of homes for plants: mountains and lowlands, river valleys and plains, ravines and plateaus. In each of these locations, differences in living conditions occur depending upon altitude and latitude. An alpine meadow with a two-month growing season differs greatly from a cypress swamp with its ten-month period for growth and production of flowers. Thus our country offers a wide variation in habitats, each with attendant characteristics of temperature, amount of sunlight, length of growing season, kind of soil; each with environmental conditions that determine which kinds of plants will grow in that particular place.

2

These two facts—the occurrence of hereditary differences in plants, and the presence of varying combinations of living conditions in each type of habitat—explain why different flowers are found in different parts of the country, and in different home environments. When a seed germinates it grows into a plant with an inherited type of root system, foliage, and flower. Seeds that germinate in a location with conditions suited to their inherent traits develop into plants that establish themselves in the habitat and make it their home. Thus a plant community made up of species that can grow in the same environment comes into existence. This necessary fitness of the environment for a particular kind of plant is often overlooked by those who transplant wild flowers to their gardens. If they are to thrive, wild species must be planted in a situation that duplicates their native habitat, so that they can continue to grow under the same combination of living conditions.

Some Important Environmental Factors

The environment of a plant is very complex, consisting of many different conditions which affect the growth and flowering of the plant. These conditions, or factors, fall into three categories: those dependent upon climate, those associated with the soil, and those caused by other living organisms. Important climatic factors are temperature, precipitation, light, and wind. Important soil factors are surface topography, soil texture, available minerals, amount of soil water, and aeration of the soil.

Temperature. Variations in temperature determine the

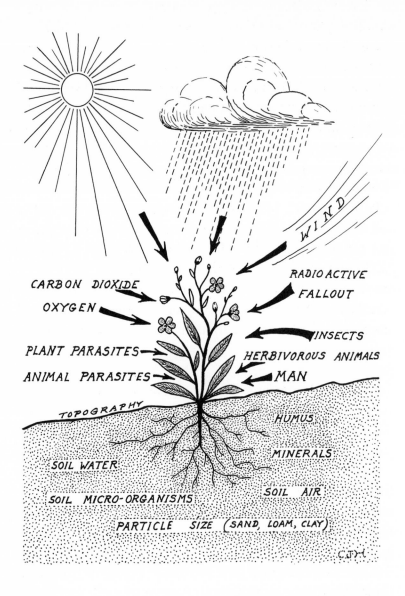

CARBON DIOXIDE

OXYGEN

PLANT PARASITES →

ANIMAL PARASITES →

WIND

RADIO ACTIVE FALLOUT

INSECTS

HERBIVOROUS ANIMALS

MAN

TOPOGRAPHY

HUMUS

MINERALS

SOIL WATER

SOIL MICRO-ORGANISMS

SOIL AIR

PARTICLE SIZE (SAND, LOAM, CLAY)

The environment of a plant is very complex, consisting of many different conditions which affect its growth and flowering.

distribution of plant life over large areas. Thus cold-climate plants that can survive in Canada and Alaska grow on our high mountains and in our northern states. Such plants have inherited a make-up of leaves, root systems, and reproductive habits suited for life in extremes of low temperature. In the same way, warm-climate plants adapted for life in Mexico and the lands to the south of us can live in our southern tier of states. These plants have characteristics of leaf, stem, root, and flower adapted for life under mild temperature conditions.

In most plants, active food manufacture and growth, as well as flower formation, can take place only between 35 and 110 degrees Fahrenheit. Lower and higher temperatures are usually fatal to all plants but those in a resting condition. Even within these limits, different plants grow best at different ranges of temperature. Some seeds germinate at lower temperatures than others, some flowers mature earlier in spring than others. Skunk cabbage often pushes its hood through partly frozen earth while snowdrifts still linger in the shaded ravines. Most plants have an inborn "thermostat" which regulates their activities; this may permit growth in only a limited range of temperatures, or it may be quite tolerant of temperature extremes. In the former case, the plant will grow in only a few habitats; in the latter, the plant, being more adaptable, will have a wider distribution. Thus an aquatic community, whether in Maine or Florida, includes pickerelweed and cattail, since these plants are adaptable to temperature extremes. But it is only in Florida that the community also includes water hyacinth, for this plant cannot live in the freezing temperatures of our northern states.

5

Precipitation. This may be either rain or snow; both are the source of the soil moisture upon which plants depend. The amount of precipitation determines the three main types of vegetation found in the United States: forest, grassland, and desert. Considerable rainfall or snow, twenty inches or more annually, is needed to sustain tree growth. The forests east of the Mississippi River, in the western mountains, and on the Pacific coast are areas receiving at least this amount of precipitation. Moderate rainfall of ten to twenty inches annually, characteristic of the region between the Mississippi River and the Rocky Mountains, is insufficient for forest growth, hence the vegetation of our central states is chiefly grassland, or prairie. Ten inches or less of rainfall, typical of the southwestern United States, creates deserts where the only plants that can survive are those highly specialized in the ability to get along with a minimum of water. The forested portions of our country provide shaded, moderately moist, protected habitats in which thrive many wild-flower communities not found in treeless regions.

Light. This factor is less important than either temperature or precipitation in influencing the distribution of plants over extensive areas. But in a more limited space, such as a hillside or a wooded glade, light is often very significant. Some species of plants have broad thin leaves adapted for manufacturing food in dim light; this is true of lady's slipper and wood sorrel. Other species require light of greater intensity, as do sunflowers and asters. It would be unusual to find sunflowers in a forest, or wood sorrel in a sunny field. Plants differ in the amount of light required for the production of flowers; some need long

6

hours of daylight for flowering while others can produce flowers in regions with comparatively short days.

Wind. The role of wind is important because it increases water loss from plants. This water loss, known as transpiration, takes place because water vapor escapes from the many minute openings, or stomates, on the surface of leaves. Stomates are necessary for the intake of carbon dioxide from the air, a gas essential for the manufacture of food by green plants. Thus some water loss via the stomates is unavoidable. However, the greater the water loss from a plant, the more water it must absorb from the soil.

Plants growing in shaded, humid habitats, or in places where there is little air movement, have a low transpiration rate. But in surroundings with low humidity, intense sunlight, or high winds, transpiration may be so great as to endanger the life of the plant. Conditions promoting excessive transpiration exist on mountain slopes, in open fields, on roadside banks, and in deserts. Some plants are endowed with features that offset this transpiration hazard: small leaves, as in alpine plants; hairy surfaces protecting the stomates, as in mullein: impervious waxy outer coverings, as in checkerberry or wintergreen. An extreme adaptation is the complete elimination of leaves; this has taken place in the cacti. Plants with any of these modifications can establish homes in habitats where the transpiration rate is high, while plants lacking them cannot. Wind also exerts a physical change in plants, reducing the amount of foliage and stems exposed aboveground, and blowing away the soil so that plants become uprooted. High winds in sandy areas, as on dunes, move the soil so

7

rapidly that only quick-growing, deep-rooted plants can maintain an anchorage. Such plants, many of them grasses, are often used to prevent erosion.

Topography. Surface contours become important when they affect the stability of the soil and its exposure to sunlight. Very steep slopes can become a plant habitat only for those species with unusually tenacious root systems, as is characteristic of many roadside weeds. On the other hand, the flat expanse of a river plain exposes plants to flooding; species living in such habitats must have an ability to grow in soil periodically saturated with water. Slopes also affect the habitat by providing varying degrees of sunlight and warmth. Wooded slopes facing south make an ideal home for early flowering wild flowers because of the higher temperature of air and soil. In such homes we can expect to find the first hepaticas and mayflowers. Fewer spring flowers grow on north-facing slopes, which get less sunlight and where the soil stays cold, or even frozen, late into spring. However, many wild flowers bloom later in the year; in summer, south-facing slopes are hot and dry while north-facing slopes are cooler and moister. Under such conditions, the north slope is a more desirable home for most wild flowers.

Soils. Soils vary in the size of the particles of which they are made. The size of the particles in turn determines the relative amount of air and water in the soil. Clay soil consists of extremely small particles, separated by minute air spaces which are easily clogged with water. As a result drainage is poor, air is lacking, and roots suffer from an oxygen deficiency. In clay soils we find plants that are able to grow in wet, poorly drained ground, such as blue

8

flag and swamp buttercup. Sandy soil, on the other hand, is made up of extremely large particles, separated by large air spaces through which water passes quickly. Sandy soils have an abundance of air but the rapid drainage often makes them dry even in regions of heavy rainfall. Yellow star-grass and mayflower prefer well drained, sandy soils. Most woodland flowers are adapted for growing in a combination of sand and clay, known as loam. Gravelly and rocky soils are not suitable for most wild flowers; two species which do grow in such habitats are field chickweed and bindweed.

The mineral content of the soil is important in several ways. Minerals are essential for growth of plants, and too small amounts of certain elements eliminate some species of wild flowers from the habitat. As an example, peaty soils are deficient in nitrogen and thus support only those plants capable of living on small amounts of this element, or of getting the nitrogen from another source. The latter course has been adopted by the insect-eating plants such as sundews and pitcher plants. These plants grow in nitrogen-poor habitats, supplementing their nitrogen intake by absorbing the organic remains of the animals they trap. Minerals also determine whether soils become alkaline or acid; some wild flowers grow best in alkaline, limestone soils, others in acid ones. Another component of soils is humus, the organic debris of leaves and other plant parts which accumulates on the forest floor. Humus is essential for the growth of colorless plants, or saprophytes, which, being unable to manufacture their own food, must get it from the soil. This is why Indian pipes are found only in rich woods with ample humus in the soil.

The amount of air in the soil, as we have seen, is a significant factor. The more saturated a soil is, the less air—and hence oxygen—it can hold. This hinders root growth. For this reason flooding the soil of woodlands or fields often kills the plants growing there by depriving the roots of the oxygen provided in their normal habitat. Some plants can grow in soils with less oxygen than other plants need. Oxygen is also vital for seed germination, though here again the essential quantity varies. Seeds of aquatic plants, such as water lilies, can germinate under conditions of low oxygen concentration where the seeds of other plants would find the amount insufficient for sprouting.

Plants must adjust themselves not only to all these physical conditions of their surroundings, but also to living with other plants and with animals in the same community. In every habitat there is competition for water, sunlight, and growing space. If a newcomer into a plant community proves capable of producing a bigger root system or more foliage, or reproducing more effectively by its type of flower or seed, it may soon crowd out the original residents. This is especially true in fields and waste places. Many flowers that have been introduced from other countries have such traits, and are able to grow in dry habitats with poor soil. As a result, these immigrants often take over a habitat and rapidly become weeds. The number of such introduced weed wild flowers is surprising, as the accompanying list shows.

The most important animals in the flowering-plant community are the insects, since the majority of our wild flowers are insect-pollinated. If the pollinating insects dis-

10

OUR WILD-FLOWER IMMIGRANTS

Bladder Campion	Heal-all
Bouncing Bet	Hop Clover
Bull Thistle	King Devil
Butter-and-Eggs	Lady's Thumb
Celandine	Mallow
Chicory	Marshmallow
Coltsfoot	Moneywort
Cow Vetch	Mullein
Daisy	Queen Anne's Lace
Dandelion	Red Clover
Dayflower	Tansy
Daylily	Viper's Bugloss
European Cowslip	Water Hyacinth
Forget-me-not	Wild Mustard
Hawkweed	Yarrow

appear, the flowers will not produce seeds and the species will die out, no matter how well adapted to the environment it otherwise may be. Herbivorous mammals are not an important factor since few find the foliage of wild flowers a satisfying diet. Their chief role is often the transport of seeds of fruits which they have eaten, of spiny burrs which stick to their fur; thus they aid in plant dispersal. The greatest threat to wild flowers comes from man himself. Forest fires and careless removal of trees from wooded areas, real-estate developments in regions of unusual plants, drainage of swamps, and other changes coincident with the march of civilization have altered many plant communities. Thoughtless picking or uprooting of wild flowers has eliminated many rare or unusual species which do not reproduce rapidly. Thus when you find wild flowers, enjoy them where they grow and disturb them as little as possible. Many kinds of orchids, mayflowers, and the smaller cacti are examples of plants that have been exterminated by man in much of their original habitat. Fortunately, conservation of the less common wild flowers is gaining increasing attention. In every state certain wild flowers are now protected by law or by interested groups.

Plant Communities

This survey of the various factors that determine the living conditions in a particular habitat show what a delicate balance exists between the environment and the plant community. Wherever all the factors are the same, similar habitats will exist with similar plant communities. These may be near one another, or they may be many miles apart; plant communities with similar wild flowers may be found in Maine, Ohio, and Michigan. However, if similar habitats are separated by barriers that prevent migration of plants from one to the other, and if the plants have not been introduced by man, the wild-flower communities with similar living conditions may have different members. The Rocky Mountains present such a barrier; as a result, habitats with the same environmental factors in Illinois and California include a number of species peculiar to each region. Thus in later chapters when we give the range of a wild flower, you will notice that many of the eastern and central states have the same species, or closely related ones; west of the Rocky Mountains, the flowers are often very different.

Two major factors determine the type of flower community you will encounter: the temperature and the amount of water in the environment. The temperature factor becomes very noticeable as one travels north and south along the Atlantic coast. In woods of New York and New England, we find such flowers as Canada mayflower and painted trillium. A few hundred miles south, in the woods of the Maryland-Virginia region we find southern harebell and leopard lily. Still farther south, we meet centaury and blue-eyed Mary. Temperature is also conditioned by the altitude. Thus the mountains of Tennessee and the Carolinas have plant communities similar to those of the lowlands of New England. As we explore the plant communities in following chapters, we must keep in mind the latitude and the altitude of the region we are visiting, since it influences the temperature of the habitat to a vital degree, and thus the kinds of flowers that can grow there.

The other major factor in determining the type of plant community is the amount of water available. Root, stem and leaf structure of plants, and their flower and fruit characteristics are often correlated with their water needs. Three types of plants can be defined in terms of their water relations: hydrophytes, mesophytes, and xerophytes. Plants which are adapted for growing in or near water, or in soils with a maximum amount of water, are known as *hydrophytes*. These are the aquatic plants found in the plant communities of streams and ponds, and the swamp-dwelling plants of pond margins as well as wet fields. Plants that are adapted for a moderately moist environment are known as *mesophytes*. They form the communities of woods and thickets where soil moisture conditions are neither too wet nor too dry. Plants which form communities in open fields, on roadsides, and in extremely dry habitats such as deserts are known as *xerophytes*. They are adapted to withstand excessive transpiration loss.

Hydrophytic communities are found both in and near the water. Aquatic plants, such as water lilies and water hyacinth, are the most extreme of hydrophytes. Others live out of the water, at least most of the time, forming communities in swamps, along stream margins, and in low wet woods or fields. Typical members of such a community are forget-me-not, Jack-in-the-pulpit, iris, and canna. The insect-eating plants are members of the hydrophytic community.

Mesophytic communities are found in the woods, or in moist fields and roadside ditches. The more mesophytic woodland flowers, such as violets, prefer rich soil in shaded woods; the less mesophytic species, such as saxifrage, grow on drier rocky slopes. The list of such mesophytic woodland flowers is a long one. It includes such familiar woodland species as hepatica, bloodroot, spring beauty, May apple, Solomon's seal, shooting star. In wooded habitats where the soil includes an abundance of humus we can find such saprophytes as Indian pipe in the East, snow plant in the West.

Xerophytic communities are the familiar ones of fields and roadsides, where there is ample sunlight and often very little soil water. A large number of the wild flowers

The moist soil and protective shade of the forest encourages the development of mesophytes such as this community of dogberry.

The rocky soil and intense sunlight of arid, treeless regions is the home of xerophytes such as this community of cacti.

in such communities are the introduced weed species, listed on page 11. Wild flowers with xerophytic adaptations present spectacular displays: the fields of owl's clover and scarlet bugler in California, the bluebonnets in Texas, the sunflowers in Kansas, the roadside asters and goldenrods in New England. Most completely xerophytic are the desert wild flowers which add color to the otherwise sandy and barren deserts after the spring rains.

Plants, like people, differ in their adaptability to living conditions. Some are very particular about their home surroundings, and live in restricted habitats where the living conditions have very fixed limits. Others are more venturesome and can be found in a wider range of habitats. Thus it is difficult to state exactly where many of our wild flowers can be found, for individuals in many species seem able to move into homes slightly different from those where most of their close relatives live. Thus some hydrophytes, like skunk cabbage and cattails, may be found living amid mesophytes in a damp woods. On the other hand, some xerophytes such as hawkweed may be found in dry woods and clearings, surrounded by mesophytes. In general, however, it would be unusual to find a xerophyte growing amid hydrophytes, or a hydrophyte growing side by side with a xerophyte.

This is the picture of the environment in which our wild flowers live, and of the conditions which surround them in their homes. The solitary lady's slipper in the wooded shade, the clump of forget-me-nots by a stream, the masses of lupine in a sunny field, the graceful wood lily in the forest glade—each is a member of a plant community with definite living conditions. Each is adapted to a certain amount of sunlight, of humidity, of soil water and soil minerals, of summer and winter temperatures. As we meet the flowers in the various plant communities, we will discover what these adaptations are, and how each wild flower is adjusted to the home in which it is found.

The leaves of pitcher plant do double duty. They carry on photosynthesis and thus manufacture food, but they also function as living traps for catching insects and other small animals, adding variety to the plant's diet.

CHAPTER TWO

HOW WILD FLOWERS DIFFER IN STRUCTURE

The habitat of a wild flower is one feature that helps in identifying it, since most plants prefer a certain type of environment for their home. Every plant living in this kind of habitat has certain characteristics that are hereditary. Such fixed traits, repeated from generation to generation, are a means of identifying individual species. We must know what these traits are if we wish to identify the flowers that make up the plant communities of each habitat.

Identifying a flower is easy if one knows how to go about it. There are two ways of doing this. An unscientific way is to compare the unknown flower with illustrations in a book. This hit-or-miss method, which at first seems the easier, presents several difficulties. A major drawback is that few books are so completely illustrated as to include every kind of flower. We have already discovered that

19

there are several thousand species even in a single state. Another disadvantage results from the fact that no two flowers of the same species are exactly alike; as a result the illustration may not be sufficiently like the specimen to permit certain identification. To these drawbacks is added the fact that identification often requires a knowledge of the entire plant, its general habit, foliage, and fruit —not usually combined in a single drawing or photograph. Such difficulties as these make the unscientific method time-consuming and a frustrating way of identifying wild flowers.

The second method is more scientific. This follows the same procedure that a detective uses in tracing the identity of his suspect. It means looking for certain clues in a systematic fashion so that nothing will be overlooked; the presence or absence of each clue helps to eliminate suspects and eventually narrows the choice to the correct individual. The detective uses such clues as fragments of hair or clothing, blood traces, and fingerprints. In the same way, scientific identification of a flower means looking for certain clues amid the many and confusing characteristics which may have no significance. In noting these clues the naturalist, like the detective, must be a careful observer with a keen eye for details. The Sherlock Holmes analogy may be carried even further, since the use of a hand lens or magnifying glass is often necessary to see details which escape the unaided eye.

The use of the scientific method may seem difficult because of the special vocabulary involved. However, in every specialized activity certain technical terms are necessary, belonging to the terminology peculiar to that activity.

Golf and baseball have their special vocabularies which a sports fan learns quickly. Fishing and photography likewise have their special terminology. Scientific activities also have a vocabulary, actually no more difficult to pronounce or understand than those of many nonscientific pursuits. Scientific terminology is time-saving since it describes concisely a particular structure or function. Botany, including flower identification, has its own terminology which is necessary to know if the scientific method of identifying flowers is to be used. This vocabulary actually makes identification easier and far more accurate. An encouraging aspect is that, once these terms are mastered, even the amateur botanist can use any flower or garden book with understanding.

Correct identification requires an ability to know what is important about the plant in question. This means knowing what clues to look for. These clues can be arranged in four groups. As you try to identify the flower, systematically check the clues in each of these groups. The four types of clues are those based on (1) flower characteristics, (2) stem characteristics, (3) leaf characteristics, and (4) fruit characteristics. These clues are found on various parts of the plant, thus one should have the whole plant, not just the flower, for an accurate identification.

Flower Characteristics

Flowers are the reproductive organs of plants. Their function is to produce seeds which eventually will grow into a new generation of plants. The structures and methods by which flowers produce seeds are quite varied, but remarkably constant for each species. Hence basic differences in the flower itself furnish valuable clues to its identity. But before we look for clues in the flower, we should know what is meant by the term "flower." The popular idea of a flower is a colorful, conspicuous, and usually fragrant part of a plant. Many flowers, however, do not fit this description; instead they are green, inconspicuous, and odorless. Such is true of ragweed, Solomon's seal, and cattail. On the other hand, many colored parts of plants that are called flowers are actually colored leaves as are the white bracts beneath the cluster of bunchberry flowers, or the "pulpit" of the Jack-in-the-pulpit.

A typical flower consists of four parts: pistils, stamens, sepals, and petals. The buttercup is a good example of a typical flower. The *pistils* occupy the center of the flower; in a general sense a pistil can be considered the female part of the flower. Its enlarged base is an ovary in which the plant eggs are produced. Above the ovary, the pistil becomes a slender stalk or style, terminating in an enlarged portion known as the stigma. The stigma functions as a landing platform for pollen grains. In some flowers the stigma is conspicuous by being large or projecting beyond the rest of the flower; in blue flag it is colored and petal-like. Surrounding the pistils are the *stamens,* which in the same general sense may be considered the male part of the flower. Each stamen consists of a slender stalk terminating in an anther. Within the anther are produced the minute pollen grains needed for fertilizing the plant eggs in the ovary. The stamens of some flowers are very conspicuous; in meadow rue they are white and the most

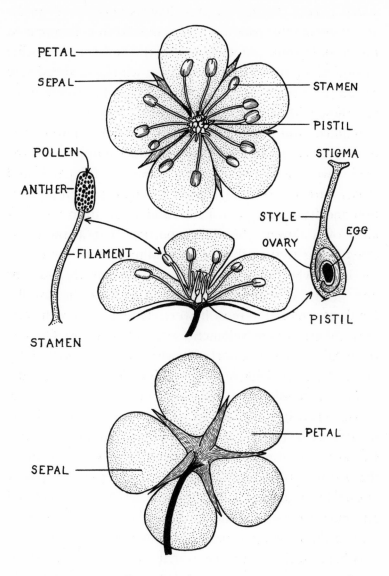

PETAL

SEPAL

STAMEN

PISTIL

POLLEN

ANTHER

STIGMA

STYLE

EGG

OVARY

FILAMENT

PISTIL

STAMEN

PETAL

SEPAL

A typical flower consists of four structures: an outer perianth made up of petals and sepals and an inner region made up of stamens and pistils. The tip of the stamen (anther) produces pollen grains; the base of the pistil (ovary) produces the eggs, or ovules.

showy part of the flower. Most flowers possess both pistils and stamens; this condition exists in wild rose, poppy, and fireweed. In some plants, however, the flower lacks pistils; in others, stamens; this is the case with arrowhead and cattail. Flowers with pistils only are called pistillate flowers; those with stamens only, staminate flowers.

Stamens and pistils are essential parts of a flower since they produce the reproductive cells that unite to form the seed. Two other parts of a typical flower—the petals and sepals—are not essential, but aid in bringing about pollination and fruit formation. Petals and sepals form the *perianth* of a flower, the showy portion that attracts our attention as well as that of pollinating insects. *Petals* are the inner whorl of flower parts, surrounding the stamens and pistils; collectively they are known as the corolla. Petals are colored in most flowers, though in a few species they are green as in Solomon's seal and hellebore. Outside the petals is another whorl of flower parts, the *sepals*. They are collectively known as the calyx. Sepals are usually green and smaller than the petals, serving to protect the flower when it is in bud. In species that lack petals, the sepals may be colored as in marsh marigold and hepatica. In some cases they are colored like the petals, a condition that exists in the lilies. Beneath the flower there may be a cluster of modified leaves known as bracts, often colored and more showy than the flowers themselves. This can be seen in the red-tipped bracts of Indian paint brush.

A botanist finds many clues that aid in identifying flowers in the arrangement of the flowers on the plant and in the nature of the perianth, especially the corolla. Five such clues will be helpful. These are (1) the arrangement of

The flower of wild strawberry has all four parts of a complete flower: a calyx of green sepals, a corolla of colored petals, a circle of pollen-producing stamens, and a central cluster of egg-producing pistils.

the flowers on the plant; (2) the color of the flower; (3) the number of petals; (4) the symmetry of the corolla; and (5) the degree of separateness or fusion of the petals.

Arrangement of Flowers on the Plant. Some flowers are *solitary,* growing singly on the flower stalk. This is the way dogtooth violet, lady's slipper, and columbine grow. In other plants such as trillium and spring beauty, the flowers grow in small irregular clusters of three or four. More commonly flowers are grouped in larger clusters which have a definite shape, and may consist of hundreds of small flowers. Such a cluster is known as an *inflorescence.* The type of inflorescence is an important clue, since the kind of inflorescence displayed by one flower is often characteristic of the entire family to which it belongs. The more important inflorescence types are the raceme, panicle, spike, spadix, umbel, and head.

A *raceme* consists of an elongated and unbranched central axis which bears numerous flowers, each with its own stalk. Racemes are characteristic of Canada mayflower, evening primrose, lupine, and forget-me-not. If the central axis branches to form a number of racemes, the inflorescence is known as a *panicle.* This large spreading flower cluster is typified in saxifrage and false Solomon's seal. A *spike* differs from a raceme by bearing stemless (sessile) flowers along an erect unbranched flower stalk. Spikes are often pencil-shaped or clublike with a compact mass of small flowers; such spikes occur in pickerelweed, butter-and-eggs, and cattail. If the spike has a thick fleshy stalk or axis in which the flowers may be partly buried, the inflorescence is known as a *spadix.* This type is characteristic of the Arum family, which includes skunk cabbage and

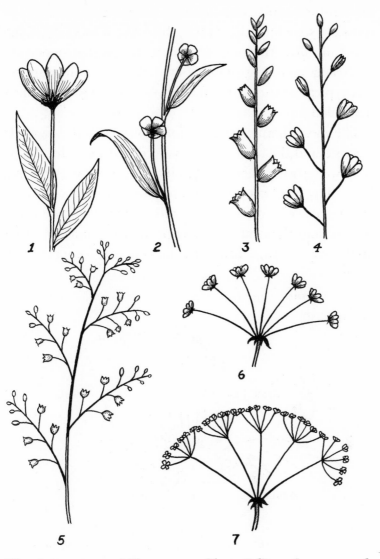

The Arrangement of Flowers on a Plant. Solitary flowers may be terminal (1) or in the axils of the leaves (axillary) as in (2). Groups of flowers may be in a spike (3), a raceme (4), a panicle (5), a simple umbel (6), or a compound umbel (7).

Jack-in-the-pulpit. The spadix is often surrounded by an accessory structure, the spathe; this is the showy white part of a calla lily. An *umbel* is a more or less flat-topped inflorescence consisting of many small flowers on short stems; it is typical of the carrot family, to which Queen Anne's lace belongs.

The most complex type of inflorescence is the *head*. It is considered the most highly evolved and specialized type of flower arrangement. A familiar example is the white daisy. The head is often mistaken for a single flower, but the "petals" of a daisy are in reality a rim of minute white flowers, and the central yellow portion is a mass of other small flowers. In a head, the flowers are compactly ar-

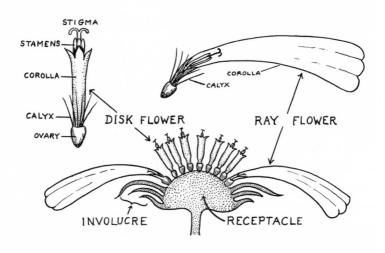

The head is a complex type of inflorescence, characteristic of a large group of wild flowers known as Composites. A typical head daisy or aster consists of a rim of ray flowers and a central mass of disk flowers, both seated on a receptacle surrounded by leafy bracts which form an involucre.

28

ranged on the broadened or cone-shaped tip of the flowering stalk. Usually the head is seated in a cluster of bracts (involucre) which, being mistaken for a calyx, also contributes to the popular idea that the daisy is a single flower. The head is characteristic of the largest group of wild flowers, the Composites; in addition to the daisy, this family includes dandelion, sunflower, aster, goldenrod, and thistle. The marginal flowers of the daisy are known as ray flowers; each has a tubular corolla with a single flat petal-like expansion. The yellow, center flowers are known as disk flowers; each disk flower has a tubular base and a toothed margin. In the dandelion, the head consists entirely of ray flowers; in a thistle, the head is made up entirely of disk flowers.

Color. Color is perhaps the most frequently used clue in identifying a flower; it is generally associated with the perianth of the flower. In a few cases the flower may lack a perianth, or it may be so insignificant as to be of little value in identification. Cattails lack a perianth, and the minute flowers of bunchberry and skunk cabbage have a much reduced perianth. But in the majority of flowers we see, the perianth is present and its color furnishes an important clue. The colored part of the perianth is usually the corolla, although in columbine, lilies, and orchids the sepals contribute color also. However, color as identification of a flower must be used with caution, for plants of the same species often differ from each other in the color of the flowers. There are, for example, hepaticas which are blue, others which are white or lavender. In addition, many white flowers tend to become pink as they mature. Yet color, though not conclusive, is the first clue we will use in tracking down the identity of the flowers we encounter in each type of habitat.

Number of Petals and Sepals. Flowers have perianths which vary in the number of sepals and petals from two or three to twenty or thirty. Most flowers have perianth parts either in threes and sixes, or in fours and fives. The three-and-six condition is characteristic of a group of plants known as *Monocots.* This includes trillium, orchid, and lily. Trillium has three green sepals and three colored petals. Orchids have three green or colored sepals and three petals, one of which is enlarged to form a sac or lip. A lily has six similar perianth parts, the sepals and petals both being colored. The four-and-five condition is characteristic of another group of plants known as *Dicots.* Among these are evening primrose (four sepals, four petals) and buttercup (five sepals, five petals). More than five petals are found in other Dicot families: water lilies and cacti may have twenty or more petals in each flower. The grouping of all flowering plants into the two main divisions of Monocots and Dicots is a basic classification used by all botanists. In the list of flower species found at the end of this book, this classification is used.

Flower Symmetry. Flowers exhibit two types of symmetry. In a buttercup, which represents one type, the corolla consists of petals which are alike in size and shape, radially arranged like the spokes of a wheel. Such radial symmetry is characteristic of a *regular* flower. Lupine or violet, representing another type of symmetry, has some petals larger than others and of a different shape. Such a corolla is symmetrical on either side of a vertical line drawn through the middle of the flower. This bilateral

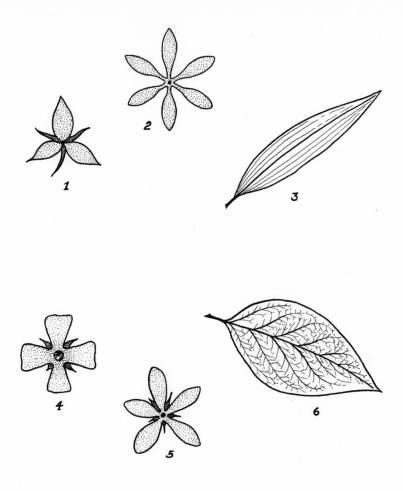

The group of Monocot wild flowers (upper row) have flowers with three petals and three sepals (1), or six perianth segments with no differentiation between petals and sepals (2), and leaves with parallel venation (3). The Dicot wild flowers (lower row) usually have flowers with four or five petals and four or five sepals (4, 5), and netted veined leaves (6).

symmetry results in an *irregular* flower. The accompanying table lists some of the more familiar wild flowers found in each type of symmetry.

SYMMETRY OF FLOWERS	
Regular Flowers	*Irregular Flowers*
(radial symmetry)	(bilateral symmetry)
Bindweed	Butter-and-eggs
Bloodroot	Cardinal flower
Buttercup	Clover
Cactus	Dutchman's breeches
Chickweed	Heal-all
Cowslip	Lady's slipper
Evening primrose	Larkspur
Five finger	Lupine
Forget-me-not	Mint
Gentian	Mullein
Lily	Orchid
Mallow	Owl's clover
Milkweed	Painted cup
Phlox	Sage
Poppy	Scarlet bugler
Queen Anne's lace	Touch-me-not
Saxifrage	Turtlehead
Water lily	Vetch
Wild geranium	Violet

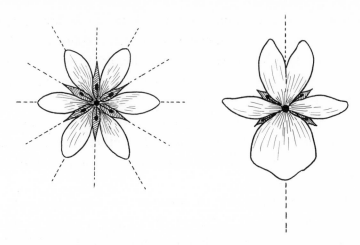

Flowers exhibit two types of symmetry. A regular flower (left) *is radially symmetrical, while an irregular flower* (right) *is bilaterally symmetrical.*

Fusion of the Petals. Another significant feature of the corolla is the degree to which the petals are separated from each other. Separate and distinct petals are characteristic of buttercup, trillium, and poppy. In some flowers the lower portion of the petals may be united, forming a tubular base to the corolla as in blue flag and Atamasco lily. When the petals are fused their entire length, a funnel-shaped corolla results with no distinction between separate petals; this is shown in bindweed. Various degrees of petal fusion can be found in such wild flowers as mayflower, evening primrose, mint, and gentian. In some, the margin is entire, in others it is toothed or lobed.

These five clues are a guide to significant differences in the flower itself. They provide a method by which the flower can be scientifically described. Summarizing the foregoing, we should take note of whether the flowers are solitary or in an inflorescence; if in an inflorescence, whether they are in a raceme, a panicle, a spike, a spadix, an umbel, or a head. Next we should look at the individual flower closely in order to note its color, whether the color is owing to sepals, to petals, or both. Then we should notice how many petals there are, whether they form a regular or an irregular corolla, and whether they are separate from each other or fused into a tubular or funnel-shaped corolla.

As an example, let us imagine we are exploring a swamp community and have discovered a plant with a spike of irregular blue flowers, with six-parted perianth. These clues lead to pickerelweed as a likely "suspect." Nearby, in the same community, is another plant, also with blue flowers but these are in racemes and each flower has a regular five-parted perianth. These clues lead to forget-me-not as another "suspect."

Stem Characteristics

It is often possible to identify a wild flower by the characteristics of the flower itself. However, other parts of the plant—its stem and growth habits, its leaves and its fruits—also contribute valuable clues. When the plant is not in flower, these additional clues are of course the only guide to identification. The size and general appearance of a plant is often owing to features of the stem. In a few species of wild flowers there is no stem, or the stem is very short; in these cases the leaves form a basal rosette or cluster from the midst of which rises the flowering stalk. Such

34

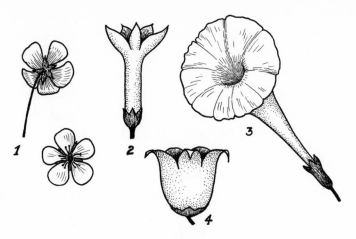

The petals of a flower may be separate (1) *or fused to varying degrees, forming a tubular corolla* (2), *a vase-shaped corolla* (3), *or an urn-shaped one* (4).

stemless plants include dogtooth violet, moccasin flower, dandelion, and saxifrage. The majority of wild flowers, however, have stems that raise the foliage and flowers far above the ground. This is an advantage in reaching toward the light, and presenting a flower display to attract pollinating insects. When a stem is present, it furnishes a few clues that aid in plant identification. These are: (1) whether the stem is upright or trailing, and (2) whether any special features are present such as an unusual shape in cross section, whether it is smooth or hairy, and the nature of its sap.

Growth Habits of Stems. Erect stems may be unbranched or branched, and grow to varying heights above the ground. Some, such as heal-all and violet, reach only a few inches upward; others grow to a height of several feet, as in the aster and daisy. A few grow seven and eight

35

feet tall, the height of meadow rue and water parsnip. In contrast to such erect stems are those which grow prostrate on the ground, or climb over other plants for support. Creeping and trailing plants with such vinelike habits include checkerberry, partridgeberry, mayflower, bindweed, and vetch.

Other Features of Stems. Other features of stems present additional clues. Most stems are round, as those of blue flag and cattail. Other stems have winglike edges, seen in blue-eyed grass, or are square, a condition typical of monkeyflower and mint. Likewise, most stems are smooth. But the stems of a few species are bristly or spiny, as in thistle, tearthumb, and prickly poppy. Other stems are hairy, as those of wild ginger and mullein. The sap of most plants is watery and colorless. But in a few species it is characteristically milky or colored, as in bloodroot and poppy, milkweed and dandelion.

Leaf Characteristics

A typical leaf consists of two parts: a thin flattened *blade* which is the leaf proper, and a supporting stalk or *petiole*. If the petiole is lacking, the leaf is sessile, a condition occurring in bellwort and evening primrose. A large vein, or *midrib*, extends the length of the blade from the petiole to the tip. Smaller veins extend from the base of the blade and from the midrib, forming a supporting framework for the leaf. Leaves, like flowers, have certain hereditary features that are characteristic of each species of wild flower. These can be used as additional clues to the plant's identity. Five clues based on leaf features are: (1) the way the leaves are arranged on the stem; (2) the pattern formed by the veins in the blade; (3) the type of leaf blade; (4) its shape; and (5) its margin.

Arrangement of Leaves on the Stem. Leaves arise from stems in one of three ways. In some species the leaves grow singly, one leaf at each point (node) of the stem. Such leaves are said to be *alternate*. Alternate leaves are characteristic of most wild flowers, among them buttercup and fireweed. In other species the leaves grow in pairs, two arising at opposite sides of the same node. These are *opposite* leaves, a feature of gentians and pinks. In a few plants three or more leaves appear at the same node; such leaves are *whorled*. A whorl of leaves is typical of Indian cucumber root and wood lily.

Leaf Venation. Two main types of venation, or arrangement of the veins in the blade, can be found in wild flowers. In one type, known as *netted venation,* the veins extend from the midrib and base of the blade to form an irregular branching network. This is typical of plants in the Dicot group; thus it is characteristic of buttercup, mallow, milkweed, aster, and daisy. In the second type, known as *parallel venation,* the main veins radiate from the base of the blade and extend parallel to the margin and the midrib. In some cases this type of venation results in a strongly pleated leaf. Such parallel venation is typical of plants in the Monocot group, particularly lily and orchid.

Simple Versus Compound Leaves. In most plants the leaf blade is in one piece; if there are indentations they do not extend to the midrib. This is known as a *simple* leaf;

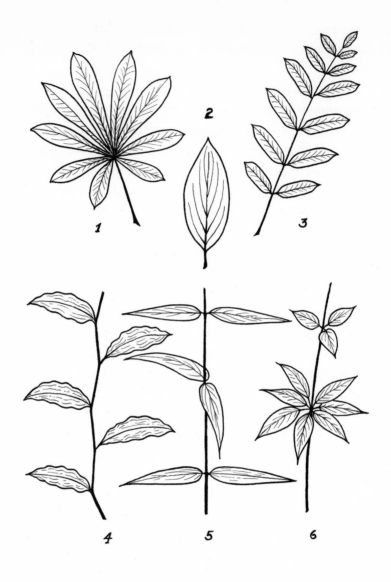

Leaf Types (upper row): *simple leaf* (2), *palmately compound leaf* (1), *and pinnately compound leaf* (3). *Arrangement of Leaves: alternate* (4), *opposite* (5), *and whorled* (6).

it is characteristic of most wild flowers, among them violets, lilies, and asters. In other plants the leaf blade is divided into sections or leaflets, attached to the central axis or midrib by individual short stalks. This type is called a *compound* leaf. Some compound leaves have the leaflets arranged like the fingers of a hand, radiating from the base of the blade. This results in a palmately compound leaf, typical of lupine and five-finger. Other compound leaves have leaflets in pairs, arranged like the barbs of a feather. This forms a pinnately compound leaf, typical of vetch and other members of the pea family. In some wild flowers, such as wood betony and yarrow, the leaflets of the blade are again divided into lobes; the result is a finely dissected, fernlike leaf.

Leaf Shape. The shape of a leaf, regardless of its size, is surprisingly constant. Clues based on the shape of the leaf are often a great aid in identifying a plant; these clues require an understanding of certain descriptive terms that have precise meanings. A *linear* leaf is grasslike, much longer than broad and tapering to a slender tip. Linear leaves are characteristic of cattail and iris. Slightly broader leaves which also taper to a sharp tip are known as *lanceolate* leaves; this shape is typical of the blades of fireweed and false Solomon's seal. *Oblong* leaves are longer than they are broad, with parallel sides and rounded tips; representative of this type is dogberry. *Elliptic* leaves, as in lady's slipper, taper to a rounded tip and base. *Ovate* leaves are egg-shaped; skunk cabbage leaves are of this type. Other terms applied to leaf shapes are *orbicular* (water lilies), *cordate* (wild ginger), and *sagittate* (arrowhead).

Leaf Margin. The type of leaf margin is also a valuable

39

recognition feature. Here again the clues involve knowing the meaning of some technical descriptive terms. If the margin is continuous, the leaf is *entire;* entire leaves are typical of lily, orchid, fireweed, and phlox. If the margin is minutely toothed, as in mallow, the leaf is said to be *serrate.* A leaf with a wavy margin is *crenate,* a condition typical of bloodroot. Indentations of the margin result in numerous types of *lobed* leaves. Indentations which converge toward the base of the blade result in a palmately lobed leaf, as in wild geranium and May apple. If the indentations extend parallel to each other toward the midrib, the leaf is pinnately lobed, as is found in thistle and dandelion. It is easy to mistake a deeply lobed leaf of either category, for a compound leaf; hence careful observation has to be made in using this clue.

These clues suggest what aspects of the leaf one should observe particularly. Summarizing them, we should take

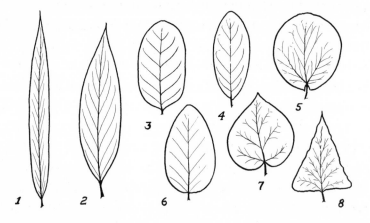

Variations in Leaf Shape: linear (1), *lanceolate* (2), *oblong* (3), *elliptical* (4), *round or orbicular* (5), *egg-shaped or ovate* (6), *heart-shaped or cordate* (7), *triangular or deltoid* (8).

40

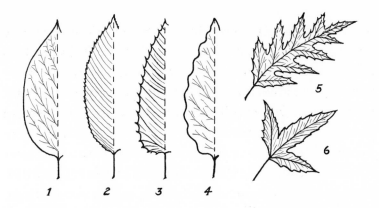

Variations in Leaf Margin: entire (1), *minutely toothed or serrate* (2), *coarsely toothed or dentate* (3), *wavy-margined or crenate* (4), *pinnately lobed* (5), *and palmately lobed* (6).

note of whether the leaves are alternate, opposite, or whorled; and whether they are simple or compound. If the leaf is simple, we should notice whether it has netted or parallel venation, whether it is linear, lanceolate, ovate, or any other shape we have described, also whether the margin is entire, toothed, or lobed.

Again, let us return to the swamp community. We find a plant with unrecognized yellow flowers; the leaves are opposite and simple, with netted venation and lanceolate blades with entire margins. These clues all point to swamp candles as a possibility. Another unrecognized yellow flower has alternate simple leaves with netted venation, but with cordate leaf blades and a crenate margin. This set of clues leads to marsh marigold.

41

Fruit Characteristics

Most wild flowers have bloomed and disappeared by late summer. In their place is a variety of fruits, each as typical of a particular species as the flower itself. Many fruits are inconspicuous and identified only by very technical features. Other fruits are familiar to us as we explore the autumn woods and fields. The fruits of wild flowers are usually of two types: fleshy and dry. The fleshy fruit most frequently encountered is that known as a *berry,* in which some or all of the ovary wall enlarges and becomes a fleshy substance surrounding the seeds. Berries are variously colored, but most are either blue or red. The accompanying table lists the most common wild flowers with berry fruits.

FLOWERS WITH BERRY FRUITS

White: White Baneberry

Black: White Trillium

Yellow: May Apple

Blue: Dogberry
Indian Cucumber Root
Poke
Solomon's Seal

Red: Bunchberry
Canada Mayflower
Checkerberry
Cranberry
False Solomon's Seal
Jack-in-the-Pulpit
Partridgeberry
Red Baneberry
Red Trillium
Skunk Cabbage
Twisted Stalk

FLOWERS WITH DRY FRUITS

Achenes: Anemone
Buttercup
Dandelion
Five-Finger
Hepatica
Meadow Rue

Pods: Cardinal Flower
Clover
Dutchman's
Breeches
Lupine
St.-John's-Wort
Tick Trefoil
Vetch

Capsules: Bloodroot
Canada Lily
Evening
Primrose
Iris
Moccasin
Flower
Touch-Me-Not
Wild Geranium
Wood Betony
Wood Lily
Wood Sorrel

Follicles: Columbine
Dogbane
Marsh
Marigold
Milkweed

Dry fruits result from the ovary becoming a hard, thin, and usually inedible covering for the seed. Such fruits are primarily adapted for dispersal by wind or by hooking onto animals' fur or persons' clothing. The simplest dry fruit is an *achene,* formed from an ovary with a single ovule. Because the seed occupies what seems to be the entire fruit, achenes are often mistaken for seeds. The fruit of a buttercup is a simple achene, as is that of the sunflower. Some achenes are barbed (beggar tick), some have parachute-

43

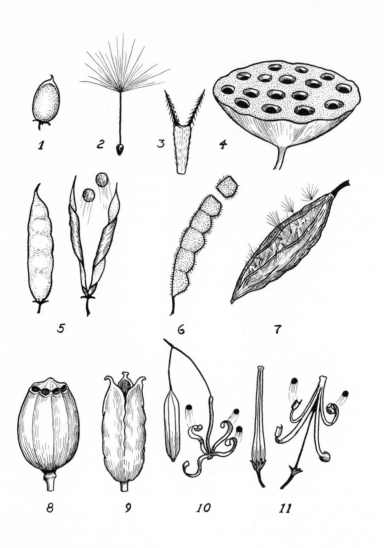

Types of Dry Fruits: achene (1), achene with hairy appendage for wind dispersal (2), barbed achene for animal dispersal (3), nutlets in a raft for water dispersal (4), pods (5, 6), follicle (7), capsules (8, 9) of poppy and iris, capsules (10, 11) of touch-menot and wild geranium.

like tufts of hairs (dandelion, hawkweed). A common type of dry fruit is the *pod,* which develops from a single pistil with a row of ovules, each of which becomes a seed. At maturity, a pod splits open along both margins. Pods are typical of the entire pea family, which includes lupine and clover. A *follicle* differs from a pod by splitting open along only one side; follicles occur in columbine and milkweed. *Capsules* develop from pistils with several compartments; when the capsule splits longitudinally the break often comes where these compartments join each other. When the capsule of wild geranium splits open, it can eject the seeds a considerable distance. The accompanying table also lists a few of the wild flowers with dry fruits of various types.

We are now ready to explore the homes of our wild flowers. We shall discover differences in the factors, such as amount of water and intensity of light, which provide the environment for the wild flowers we may see. We shall meet what, at first sight, may seem a bewildering variety of wild flowers. However, if we remember to look for the clues that have been suggested here, the wild-flower community will resolve itself into individuals each with its own distinctive traits.

The minute brown flowers of cattails are borne in a cylindrical inflorescence whose lower portion is a compact plushlike mass of pistillate flowers, and whose slender, terminal portion consists of staminate flowers.

CHAPTER THREE

FLOWERS AT HOME
IN THE WATER

Wild flowers are most often found on land. A small number, however, are aquatic, adapted for life as hydrophytes. These are at home in or near fresh water, living in streams, ponds, and lakes. Many of these plants have special features that enable them to live in aquatic or semi-aquatic habitats. These adaptations occur in leaves, stems, roots, and even in methods of pollination and seed dispersal.

In some hydrophytes the leaves are completely submerged. Such leaves, if simple, are thin and ribbonlike; if compound, they are divided into threadlike leaflets and subdivisions. Submerged leaves, like aerial leaves, are the food-manufacturing organs of the plant, carrying on photosynthesis whereby carbon dioxide and water are converted into carbohydrates. Submerged leaves obtain the carbon dioxide from the air dissolved in the water, which diffuses into the plant through the outer permeable tissues of the leaves. In other hydrophytes the leaves float on the surface of the water; such leaves are provided with air spaces which give them buoyancy. Still another group of hydrophytes raises their leaves on long petioles or stiff stems so that all or part of the blade is above water.

The stems of hydrophytes with floating leaves are often elongated and ropelike, permitting the leaves to reach the surface even though the roots may be buried in the mud or sand five feet below. The stems of some aquatic plants are horizontal underground rhizomes which give added anchorage in the muddy bottom. Roots of submerged plants are poorly developed, since the water and minerals needed for food manufacture can easily diffuse into the underwater parts of the plant from the surrounding environment. Flowers either grow above the water on erect flower stalks, or float on the surface. In a few species the flowers are formed beneath the surface. The flower of a white water lily, after pollination, is pulled beneath the surface by a coiling of the petiole. When the seeds are ripe, the underwater seed pod bursts and the seeds rise to the surface, floating away to establish themselves in new homes.

In exploring the shore of a pond and the adjacent water, we discover that there are several different "neighborhoods" in this community. They begin in the saturated soil of the land circling the water's edge, and extend into the deep water of the pond. The land-water habitat is populated by blue flag, cattail, arrowhead, pickerelweed, and wild calla. Advancing into shallow water we find a community of plants rooted in the bottom, with a variety of leaf types. Pipewort and bladderwort have submerged leaves;

water shield has some leaves submerged and some floating; lotus lily has leaves raised above the water's surface. Progressing into deeper water, where we must swim or use a boat to reach the flowers, we find aquatics with floating leaves: purple bonnet, yellow water lily, and white water lily. Independent of the bottom is the free-floating water hyacinth which often forms green rafts, acres in extent, frequently far from shore.

Wild Flowers of Pond Margins

CATTAILS are universal members of the aquatic community. Unusual is the pond or stream margin that does not provide a home for this plant. The linear, swordlike leaves with parallel venation form impenetrable ranks, shoulder high, edging the water. They are venturesome hydrophytes, some individuals moving away from the water margin to live in wet fields and swampy woods. It may be a surprise to learn that the plushlike cylindrical spikes which rise above the leaves are flowers; each spike is made up of thousands of tiny brown flowers, each lacking a perianth and all crowded into this type of inflorescence. The flowers in the upper portion of the spike are staminate, those at the base are pistillate and, in late summer, produce fluffy nutlets that are dispersed by the wind. Cattails, widely distributed throughout North America, flower from May through July.

WILD CALLA, also known as water arum, is another hydrophyte whose flowers are minute and lack a perianth. They are clustered on a fleshy spadix beneath which grows

49

a conspicuous white spathe. Wild calla is a striking member of the pond-margin neighborhood in the cooler portions of northeastern United States and Canada. A few large simple cordate leaves form a basal cluster from which the flower stalk rises. This is a species which thrives also in cold bogs, flowering from April through July. The cultivated calla lily is a domesticated relative; skunk cabbage and Jack-in-the-pulpit are close relatives, all being members of the Arum family.

Two members of the pond-margin community have blue flowers: blue flag and pickerelweed. BLUE FLAG, or wild iris, has stiff erect stems bearing simple sword-shaped leaves

Water arum, or wild calla, a hydrophyte of bogs and cool lake shores, produces its flowers on a fleshy spadix which is enveloped by a showy white spathe.

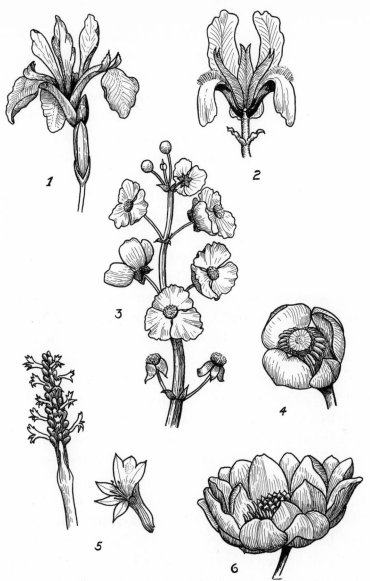

Some Conspicuous-flowered Members of the Pond Community:
Blue flag (1), *with portion of perianth removed in* (2) *to show*
three-part, petal-like style in center of flower; Arrowhead (3);
Yellow Pond Lily (4); *Pickerelweed* (5); *Lotus Lily* (6).

with parallel venation and growing to a height of several feet. It may be rooted in the mud, below the water surface, or in the wet soil adjacent to ponds and streams. Showy flowers, two to three inches in leng⁺¹ ow solitary or in small clusters at the tips of the stems. Each flower has a regular perianth of six parts; sepals and petals are all colored blue or purple, and veined with yellow and white. The sepals are broad and recurved, the smaller petals grow erect. Adding to the ornateness of the flower is a branching style which arches over the stamens and resembles three additional petals. Blue flag is in flower from late spring to early summer, and can be found throughout eastern North America. Related species—yellow, white, and blue—grow in the southern and western United States. Like cattail, blue flag grows in wet meadows and roadside ditches as well as along the margins of ponds and streams. Blue flag has familiar garden relatives in the many cultivated varieties of iris, some of which are descendants of the fleur-de-lis of Europe, others of Japanese species.

PICKERELWEED has smaller irregular blue flowers, a quarter of an inch in length, with sepals and petals colored alike. The flower has an upper and a lower lip; the upper lip is three-lobed and the lower lip has three spreading segments. The flowers are borne in a dense terminal spike at the tip of a stout erect flower stalk. The simple large heart-shaped leaves of pickerelweed are a glossy green and borne on long petioles which hold the leaves above the water. The flowers appear in spring and continue through autumn. Pickerelweed is a hardy aquatic, common throughout eastern United States, ranging north into Nova Scotia.

ARROWHEAD gets its name from the large simple leaves whose basal lobes extend backward in arrowhead fashion. Arrowhead grows to a height of three feet, producing flower stalks that bear white flowers in whorls of three. The lower whorls are made up of pistillate flowers, the upper whorls of staminate ones. Each flower has a regular perianth, about one inch in diameter, with three short-lived white petals and three persistent green sepals. Arrowhead is found throughout eastern North America, where it flowers in summer. It is also known as swamp potato because the American Indians ate the starchy rhizomes as we do potatoes. It was introduced into southern California by the Chinese, who call it tule potato and likewise use the rhizomes as food.

LOTUS LILY is the American cousin of the sacred lotus of India; it is also known as water chinquapin and duck acorn because of the nutlike fruits. Lotus lilies grow in the ponds and swampy streams of the southeastern United States; they are easily recognized by their huge circular leaves, up to twenty inches in diameter, borne aloft on stout erect stems. The flower stalks also rise above the water, bearing throughout the summer pale yellow flowers eight inches or more in diameter. Each flower has a regular perianth with numerous sepals and petals which show gradations in color from the outermost green sepals to the inner colored petals. The flower has an unusual top-shaped base which, after fertilization, becomes a flat-topped raft for the brown fruits, each seated in its own pocketlike depression. Underground parts of lotus lilies, as well as fruits, were a part of the diet of American Indians living in the southern United States.

Wild Flowers with Submerged Leaves

Wading from the pond margin into water a foot or more in depth, we may see an aquatic plant with basal tufts of narrow grasslike leaves, rooted in the sandy bottom. This is PIPEWORT, an unassuming hydrophyte whose stiff flower stalks rise pipelike above the surface of the water, each terminating in a small head of minute white flowers. One must look closely to see the several sepals and tiny three-lobed corolla of an individual flower, for each is only about an eighth of an inch in diameter. Pipewort, which is in flower from July to August, can be found throughout eastern North America.

WATER SHIELD, or fanwort, is an aquatic plant with two kinds of leaves. Some are oval or linear and float on the surface like small water lily leaves. Others, growing submerged, are compound and finely divided into threadlike segments. White flowers, about one half an inch in diameter, grow at the surface of the water. Each flower has a regular perianth of three or four sepals and an equal number of petals. Each petal has two yellow spots near the base. Water shield grows in the warmer pond communities of the southern United States. Known as fish grass, it is common in aquaria either floating in bunches or attached to the bottom.

BLADDERWORT is an aquatic plant with compound, fernlike submerged leaves; it often forms dense mats of vegetation in sluggish streams. A unique feature of bladderwort is its ability to trap small invertebrates, upon which it feeds, in small bladders among the leaves. Each bladder is equipped with a trap-door opening which per-

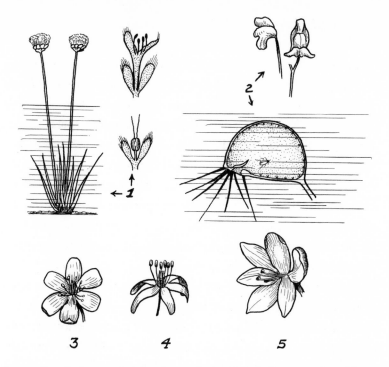

Some Small-flowered Members of the Pond Community: Pipe-wort (1) *with staminate flower* (above) *and pistillate flower* (below); *Bladderwort* (2), *with enlarged section view of the insect-catching underwater trap; Water Shield* (3); *Purple Bonnet* (4); *and single flower of Water Hyacinth* (5).

mits the animal to enter but prevents its escape. Flower stalks six to eight inches tall bear purple flowers; the corolla is irregular and two-lipped with the lower lip extended into a spur. Each flower is only a half inch in diameter. This member of the pond community is found throughout the eastern states, where it flowers from June to September. A related species with yellow flowers, being more of a land-dweller, roots in wet soil.

55

Wild Flowers with Floating Leaves

Where the water is not too deep for the stems to reach the bottom, though often far from shore, live hydrophytes with floating leaves. Of these, the smallest-flowered is **PURPLE BONNET**, whose oval leaves are three inches or less in diameter. Each leaf is attached at the center to a long wiry petiole which extends downward to a submerged rootstock. Stem, petiole, and underleaf surface are often covered with a slimy jelly. Purple flowers are borne in the axils of the leaves; each flower has a regular perianth of three or four narrow sepals and an equal number of petals. Purple bonnet, which is in flower from June to September, flourishes throughout eastern North America but is especially abundant from Florida to Texas.

YELLOW POND LILY has several common names, among them cow lily and spatterdock. This familiar and widespread member of the pond community can be found throughout eastern North America, adding a touch of bright yellow to swampy coves from May to September. The round, floating leaves, growing to a diameter of twelve inches, have a cleft near the attachment of the petiole; the latter serves as a tough anchor rope holding the leaves to the rhizomes buried in the mud six feet or more beneath the surface of the water. Yellow pond lily flowers, growing to a diameter of several inches, are raised above the water on a stiff flower stalk. The regular flower consists of five or six yellow sepals, of which the outermost are often tinged with green, and of numerous small yellow scalelike petals that encircle the stamens and the base of the pistil. The conspicuous stigma has a reddish, flattened tip.

White water lily (*left*) has floating leaves and flowers, but is attached to the bottom by long wiry stems; water hyacinth (*right*) forms floating flower beds independent of the bottom.

The queen of the pond community is the WHITE WATER LILY, contributing fragrance as well as beauty with the large white flowers that reach a diameter of seven or eight inches. From June to September these water lilies form colorful floating flower gardens throughout eastern North America. The round leaves, often a foot or more in diameter, have a deep cleft near the attachment of the sinuous petiole. Each flower has a regular perianth of four narrow green sepals and numerous broader petals that are often tinted with pink. In the center of the corolla is a mass of golden-yellow stamens surrounding the central pistil.

Water lily flowers are unusual in having the perianth show a transition from true petals to petal-like stamens and finally to true stamens.

If our aquatic exploration takes us into the southeastern United States, particularly Florida and Louisiana, we can find the showy WATER HYACINTH, an immigrant from South America, which has made itself at home in the warm waters of southern lakes and sluggish rivers. Shiny oval leaves form clumps with pendant roots that trail in the water as the plant floats on the surface. When in shallow water or stranded on the mud, these roots become embedded in the soil. Each leaf has an inflated petiole which acts as a buoy in keeping the plant afloat. Ornate lavender flowers, an inch or more in diameter, have a slightly irregular, funnel-shaped perianth with the rim of the corolla lobed into six free segments. Water hyacinth flowers are clustered in a dense spike, growing to a height of a foot or more, like the height of the true hyacinth. If we consider water hyacinth only in terms of its beauty, it rates high as an addition to our aquatic plant communities. However, if our thoughts are of a practical nature, we find it necessary to fight the spread of this species and prevent its choking our waterways and obstructing navigation. The cost of controlling and eradicating the water hyacinth in Florida has earned for this hydrophyte the name "million-dollar weed."

HOW TO IDENTIFY SOME AQUATIC WILD FLOWERS

Clue No. 1. Is a perianth present or lacking?

If a perianth is lacking, go to Clue No. 2.
If a perianth is present, go to Clue No. 3.

Clue No. 2. Is a colored spathe present or lacking?

If a white spathe is present, the flower is . . . . WILD CALLA.
If a white spathe is lacking, the flower is . . . . CATTAIL.

Clue No. 3. How large is the flower?

If it is an inch or less in diameter, go to Clue No. 4.
If it is more than an inch in diameter, go to Clue No. 6.

Clue No. 4. What is the color and symmetry of the corolla?

If purple and regular, the flower is . . . . PURPLE BONNET.
If blue and irregular, the flower is . . . . PICKERELWEED.
If yellow or purple and irregular, the flower is . BLADDERWORT.
If white and regular, go to Clue No. 5.

Clue No. 5. How are the flowers arranged on the plant?

If solitary, the flower is . . . . WATER SHIELD.
If in terminal clusters, whorls of three . . . . ARROWHEAD.
If in a buttonlike head . . . . PIPEWORT.

Clue No. 6. What type of symmetry is shown by the perianth?

If irregular, with lavender flowers in a showy spike . . . .
. . . . WATER HYACINTH.
If regular, go to Clue No. 7.

Clue No. 7. What is the color of the perianth?

If white or pink, the flower is . . . . WHITE WATER LILY.
If blue or purple, the flower is . . . . BLUE FLAG.
If yellow, go to Clue No. 8.

Clue No. 8. How many perianth segments are there?

If five or six colored sepals, small scalelike petals . . . .
. . . . YELLOW WATER LILY.
If more than six sepals and petals of equal size . . . LOTUS LILY.

Jack-in-the-pulpit hides its minute flowers at the base of a spadix
within the tubular spathe which forms the conspicuous part of the
inflorescence; the tip of the spadix projects as the "Jack" at the
mouth of the spathe, or "pulpit."

CHAPTER FOUR

FLOWERS AT HOME
IN SWAMPS AND BOGS

A number of hydrophytes have homes in the water-saturated soil of swamps and bogs, wet fields and moist woods. Here they form communities which are intermediate between the aquatic ones of ponds and streams, and the mesophytic communities of woods. Members of this community have few of the special adaptations that occur in aquatic plants, but they all require an ample supply of soil water. Many are able to live in the acid and peaty environment of bogs and poorly drained woodlands. As in the aquatic community, different seasonal temperatures determine the presence or absence of certain kinds of wild flowers. Thus we find orchids in the cooler habitats of the northern United States, crinum lilies and cannas in the warmer regions of the southern United States.

The swamp-bog-wet ground community includes a great number of many common wild flowers, of which we can describe only a few of the most common species. Some of the tallest herbaceous plants—meadow rue and meadow parsnip—are members of this community, as are such early spring wild flowers as skunk cabbage and marsh marigold. This type of habitat is also the home of unique insect-eating plants: the sundew, Venus'-fly-trap, and pitcher plant. It will make our recognition of the inhabitants of this community easier if we follow the clues suggested in Chapter Two. To learn their identity, we can first group the wild flowers by their color, or the color of the accessory floral parts. Within each color group, the most useful clues are the type of inflorescence and the symmetry of the corolla.

Green or Brown Flowers

Rare is the swamp or wet meadow in eastern United States that does not display the bright green of SKUNK CABBAGE foliage early in spring. While snowdrifts are still lingering in the shadows, this pioneer among the wild flowers pushes its conical hood of mottled green and brown through the earth, even before the leaves appear. Skunk cabbage is a member of the Arum family, which has a spadix as the inflorescence, as we have already seen in wild calla. In skunk cabbage the spathe forms a hood which hides the globular spadix, on which are borne minute yellow flowers with small sepals but no petals. In late summer these flowers become a mass of brown fruits. Huge coarsely veined, cordate leaves—often several feet in length —appear after the spathes develop. When crushed, the

Skunk cabbage completely conceals its flowers within a hoodlike spathe *(left)*; when a portion of the spathe is removed *(right)*, the globular spadix and its small yellowish flowers become visible,

foliage gives off an unpleasant odor, responsible for the common name.

JACK-IN-THE-PULPIT, also known as Indian turnip because of its edible though bitter rootstock, is another member of the Arum family. This spring wild flower is common in swampy habitats and wet woods throughout eastern North America. One or two large compound leaves of three leaflets each arise on stems that grow to a height of a foot or two. The flower stalk terminates in an inflorescence consisting of a spadix and spathe, as in skunk cabbage. The "pulpit" is the green-and-purple-striped spathe, whose tubular basal portion hides most of the club-like spadix. Only the tip of the spadix projects as the "Jack" beneath the arching upper portion of the spathe. Minute yellowish flowers, lacking a perianth, are produced on the lower portion of the spadix, staminate flowers above the pistillate ones. The latter form a cluster of berries which become bright red in autumn and are visible when the spathe withers and falls off. The underground stems were boiled by the American Indians, who ate them with venison or ground them into flour.

Often found growing near skunk cabbage in wet habitats is another large and coarse-leaved plant, AMERI-

Some Green or Brown Swamp Flowers: American Hellebore (1); *Leafy Green Orchis* (2); *Jack-in-the-Pulpit* (3) *showing section through spathe and flowers at base of spadix; Skunk Cabbage* (4) *with section through spathe showing globular spadix at bottom of the "hood."*

64

CAN HELLEBORE. The strongly veined, accordion-pleated leaves are a foot or two in length and form a bushy plant that bears a branching panicle of many small yellowish-green flowers, each with a regular perianth less than an inch in diameter. Also known as Indian Poke, this common member of the hydrophytic community is one of the less colorful species in the Lily family; like others in the family, the flower consists of six segments, sepals and petals being colored alike. American hellebore is found in the northern United States and Canada, flowering in May and June; the roots are poisonous, containing a toxic substance of the alkaloid group. Grazing animals ordinarily avoid hellebore plants because of their sharp burning taste.

LEAFY GREEN ORCHIS is a stout-stemmed orchid of cold bogs and damp forests in the northern United States and Canada where it flowers in May and June. The plant reaches a height of two feet and bears large lanceolate leaves with typical Monocot parallel venation. The inflorescence is a narrow terminal spike made up of many small greenish flowers, each measuring about a quarter of an inch across. Leafy green orchis flowers are irregular, as is typical for the Orchid family. The perianth consists of three spreading sepals and three petals of which one has a blunt lip and an incurved spur.

White Flowers

In the swamp and bog community we can find white flowers of great variety and many sizes, ranging from a quarter of an inch or less in diameter to those three or four inches in length. Among the smaller flowers are meadow rue, meadow parsnip, spotted cowbane, ladies' tresses, and boneset. The larger flowers include water violet, turtle-head, spider lily, crinum lily, and showy lady's slipper.

TALL MEADOW RUE is a bushy plant of wet fields and roadside ditches, growing to a height of six or seven feet. Its frequent occurrence around marshy ponds is responsible for its other name of muskrat weed. The leaves are compound, and divided into numerous small rounded and lobed leaflets. The flowers are small but borne in great numbers in a spreading terminal panicle. Tall meadow rue is a member of the Buttercup family, and like some other wild flowers in this family, each flower consists only of sepals. These are greenish and soon drop off. The white color of the flowers is due to the conspicuous white stamens. Tall meadow rue is common throughout the eastern United States, flowering from June to September.

WATER PARSNIP, another rank-growing plant of wet habitats, often forms dense growths along roadside ditches and in wet fields throughout the United States and Canada. A stout branching stem grows to a height of seven or eight feet, bearing pinnately compound leaves made up of five to seventeen leaflets. Submerged portions of water parnip produce compound leaves with threadlike segments similar to those of aquatic plants. Numerous minute flowers, each with a five-toothed green calyx and five small white petals, are grouped in an umbel type of inflorescence. They flower from July to September.

SPOTTED COWBANE, or water hemlock, is a close relative of water parsnip. It too is a rank-growing plant of ditches and wet fields, growing six feet or more in height.

Some White Swamp Flowers: Meadow Rue (1); *Ladies' Tresses* (2) *with enlarged views of flower; Water Parsnip* (3); *Boneset inflorescence cluster* (5), *individual head* (4), *and single tubular flower* (6); *Spider Lily* (7); *Crinum Lily* (8).

The stout purple-spotted stem bears pinnately compound leaves, with the leaflets again subdivided into smaller segments. Small regular white flowers, with incurved tips to the five petals, are borne in large umbels. Spotted cowbane grows throughout eastern North America and Canada, being in flower all summer. The tuberlike roots resemble small sweet potatoes, but are very poisonous, often causing fatalities among cattle. A related, similar species occurs on the Pacific coast.

LADIES' TRESSES, an inconspicuous member of the Orchid family, grows less than a foot in height, from a cluster of lanceolate basal leaves. The resemblance of the inflorescence to a braid spiraling up the slender spike gives the plant its common name. Each flower, less than a quarter inch in length, has an irregular perianth, with three sepals and three petals. The lateral sepals are narrow, the upper one is united with the petals; one petal has a spreading tip which forms a lip to the flower. Ladies' tresses grow in cool bogs, forest swamps, and wet fields of eastern North America, flowering in June and July. An extract from the roots was used by American Indians as a blood tonic.

BONESET, or thoroughwort, is a stout-stemmed plant growing to a height of four or five feet, with deeply veined lanceolate leaves opposite each other, their basal portions encircling the stem. Boneset is a composite, thus the flowers are borne in heads. Individual flowers, only a quarter of an inch in size, are tubular with a triangular lobed margin. Each head is composed of about a dozen of these minute flowers. The heads in turn are grouped in dense flat-topped clusters. Boneset includes some forty species, the majority found along stream banks and in moist woods throughout

North America. It is in flower from July to October. A tea made from the dried leaves is considered, in many rural areas, to have considerable medicinal value.

All of the preceding white flowers are small, ranging from a half inch downward in size. Other white flowers of swampy habitats range upward from half an inch to several inches in diameter. Two have regular perianths: spider lily and crinum lily. These are southern wild flowers, found only in the warmer communities. Both are members of the Amaryllis family, and thus have six-parted perianths.

CRINUM LILY, or swamp lily, grows in wet ditches and swampy woods from Florida to Texas, flowering from May to August. Narrow linear leaves with parallel venation (the Amaryllis family belongs to the Monocot group of flowering plants) grow at the base of the plant, which reaches a height of three or four feet. A slender erect flower stalk bears a small cluster of fragrant snow-white flowers, each with a funnel-shaped base formed by the fusion of the three sepals and three petals, which are colored alike. From the center of the perianth, which reaches a diameter of several inches, rise a conspicuous central pistil and six stamens. Our American crinum lily is one of sixty species in the crinum genus, the others being tropical in their distribution.

SPIDER LILY is so named because of the narrow, elongated and often twisted perianth segments that give the flower a spidery appearance. Each flower has a tubular basal portion, as in crinum lily, but the perianth has an added feature in a white saucerlike web which unites the base of the stamens. The three sepals and three petals are similar in color and appearance. Spider lilies have linear, grasslike leaves and a flower stalk two or three feet tall, terminating in a small cluster of the showy flowers, each several inches in diameter. Spider lilies are found in the southeastern United States, and are in flower from May to August.

The remaining white flowers have irregular perianths. These include water violet, turtlehead, and showy lady's slipper. WATER VIOLET, or lance-leaved violet, is a stemless species with a basal cluster of erect lanceolate leaves from which rise long, slender, flower stalks, each terminated by a solitary violet flower. The fragrant white perianth has typical violet bilateral symmetry, with five green sepals and five colored petals. The lower petal is striped with purple and projects backward in a spur. This is an early flowering violet in bloom from March to June; it is found in wet woods and fields from New England to

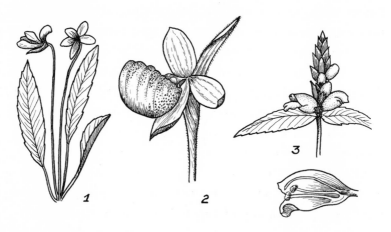

White Swamp Flowers with Irregular Perianths: Water Violet (1); Showy Lady's Slipper (2); Turtlehead (3).

Florida. A western cousin of the same color but larger in size thrives in boggy meadows of the Pacific coast.

TURTLEHEAD is well named; the profile of the irregular perianth, with the upper lip arching over the lower one, resembles a turtle's beak. Turtlehead is a plant of roadside ditches, swamps, and wet woods, growing to a height of three feet. It has simple elliptic leaves and produces flowers in a dense spikelike cluster. The corolla is two-lipped, the upper lip being concave and inflated, the lower lip slightly lobed. Turtlehead is found throughout the eastern half of the United States, flowering during the summer. A southern relative, known as snakehead, grows in wet woods and cypress forests from Maryland southward.

SHOWY LADY'S SLIPPER, a member of the Orchid family, is at home in cold bogs and forest swamps of the northern United States and Canada. It is a vivid wild flower, the aristocrat of the plant community. A stout hairy stem bears several large elliptical and pointed leaves; one or a few flowers, each several inches in length, develop on short flower stalks. The three sepals and two petals are a spotless white, but the inflated saclike lip formed by one petal is striped with crimson. The entire plant grows only to a height of a foot or two. Showy lady's slipper is in flower during June and July.

Yellow or Orange Flowers

The yellow flowers we are likely to encounter in a swamp or wet woods community are also of a variety of sizes. Some are small, one-half inch or less in diameter: swamp candles, whorled loosestrife, and orange milkwort have such small flowers. Others, such as marsh marigold, touch-me-not, and golden canna are larger, reaching lengths from three-quarters of an inch to several inches.

SWAMP CANDLES, or swamp loosestrife, makes itself at home where woods meet the shores of ponds, as well as in wet roadside habitats. Erect stems, one to two feet tall, bear opposite lanceolate leaves and terminate in a spike-like cluster of many small flowers, each about one-quarter of an inch in diameter. Each flower has a regular perianth, with five partly united green sepals and five separate and spreading yellow petals. Swamps candles grow throughout the eastern half of the United States, flowering during the summer.

A frequent associate of swamp candles is WHORLED LOOSESTRIFE, distinctive because of the square stems

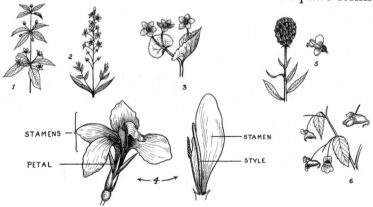

Some Yellow or Orange Swamp Flowers: Whorled Loosestrife (1); Swamp Candles (2); Marsh Marigold (3); Golden Canna (4) with enlarged view of a single stamen with its petal-like filament; Orange Milkwort (5); Touch-me-not (6).

72

and oval leaves borne in whorls of four or five. It grows to the same height as swamp candles. In the axils of the upper leaf whorls are long-stalked flowers with five spreading petals in a regular corolla. Whorled loosestrife is also a summer-flowering species of wet habitats throughout eastern North America.

ORANGE MILKWORT is a low-growing plant with a basal rosette of oblong leaves, and narrow leaves along the stem. Small flowers, about a quarter of an inch in width, are crowded into a compact spike. Each flower has an irregular perianth, with two of the five sepals large and petal-like; the three upper petals are joined, and the lower two are crested or keeled. This is a summer-flowering member of swamp and wet woodland communities of the eastern United States.

MARSH MARIGOLD, or cowslip, brightens swampy fields and woods in spring with its golden-yellow flowers. This is a hardy member of the community, being as much at home in Labrador and Alaska as in Iowa and North Carolina. Marsh marigold is a succulent, stout-stemmed, branching plant growing to a height of several feet, with large cordate or kidney-shaped leaves. It is a member of the Buttercup family, and its inch-broad flowers resemble oversized buttercups. Each flower has a regular perianth of five to fifteen glossy petal-like sepals which are yellow rather than green; there are no petals. The fleshy stems and leaves can be cooked and eaten in the same fashion as spinach. The tender unopened flower buds are often pickled and used as capers.

TOUCH-ME-NOT, also known as jewelweed or snapweed, is a rank-growing plant with succulent stems which

Marsh marigold, or cowslip, is a swamp-dwelling plant with flowers which are unusual in having the sepals colored, in place of the petals which are absent.

grow to a height of five or six feet. It lives in low wet woods and thrives in roadside ditches. Elliptical, coarsely toothed leaves grow alternately on the stems, which are enlarged at the nodes. The flowers, about an inch in width, are orange-yellow with darker spots; they hang in a horizontal position on slender stalks. The perianth is irregular; the calyx consists of three sepals, one of them spurred and colored like the petals, and the corolla consists of five petals, the lateral pair on each side being united. The flowers are clustered in a spreading panicle. This is a summer-flowering species found throughout eastern North America. The common name of touch-me-not comes from the fact that when the fruiting capsule is ripe, the slightest touch at its tip triggers an explosive mechanism whereby the capsule splits into segments and catapults the seeds away from the plant. This is one of the more unusual methods of seed dispersal exhibited by flowering plants.

GOLDEN CANNA, like crinum and spider lilies, is a subtropical member of the swamp community, being found only in the southeastern United States; its relatives have homes in Mexico and Central America. Its robust stems and large strongly veined leaves make canna popular as a foliage plant in gardens. The leaves grow to a length of several feet, and the plants reach a height of five or six feet. The flowers are borne in a small terminal cluster. Canna flowers are irregular and very showy, reaching a diameter of three or four inches. The tubular base of the perianth spreads out into three golden-yellow petals, surrounded by three erect greenish sepals. Four of the stamens are also yellow and petal-like, adding to the ornateness of the flower. Golden canna grows in wet woods and roadside ditches, flowering from late spring into summer.

Red or Pink Flowers

The red and pink flowers of the hydrophytic community all are large, showy plants. Two have regular perianths: swamp rose mallow and marshmallow. Two have irregular perianths; these are oswego tea and cardinal flower.

SWAMP ROSE MALLOW is a tall marsh plant with rank-growing stems that reach a height of six to seven feet, and large ovate leaves that are coarsely toothed. It is an

75

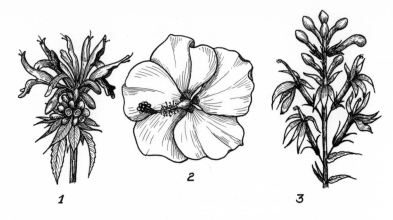

Some Red or Pink Swamp Flowers: Oswego Tea (1); *Swamp Rose Mallow* (2); *Cardinal Flower* (3).

unusual wild flower in that it can live in the saline environment of the coastal marshes found along the eastern coast of the United States. The flowers are extremely large, reaching a diameter of six inches. A calyx of five green sepals, united at their base, supports a regular corolla of five separate petals that vary in color from white to cream, with red or crimson tints in the lower portion of each petal. In the swamp rose mallow, as in its close relative, the garden hibiscus, the perianth has a cylindrical column at the center, formed by the fused stamen stalks which completely surround the lower part of the pistil. Swamp rose mallow blooms from July through September.

MARSHMALLOW, also with either pink or white flowers, is likewise a marsh plant of both fresh and brackish waters of the eastern United States. Its tall leafy stem, growing up to six feet in height, bears conspicuously veined ovate leaves which are three-lobed and terminate in a

76

cluster of flowers. The flowers, which appear in July and continue in bloom through October, have the same floral structure as that of swamp rose mallow but are slightly smaller in size. The roots are the source of a mucilaginous substance used as the base of marshmallow paste and many medicines. A cultivated relative is the garden hollyhock.

OSWEGO TEA, or bee balm, is a square-stemmed plant growing to a height of three feet with opposite leaves that are oval and coarsely toothed. The scarlet flowers form a brilliant contrast to the lush greenery of the moist meadows and stream banks where this wild flower grows. The flowers are in a compact terminal cluster, seated amid green and red, leafy bracts. Each flower, about one inch in length, has an irregular perianth. The tubular calyx is edged with five teeth that extend into hairlike tips; the two-lipped corolla has an arching upper lip and a spreading three-lobed lower lip. Oswego tea, a member of the Mint family, flowers during the summer; it occurs throughout the eastern United States.

CARDINAL FLOWER is another scarlet flower of wet habitats, growing to the same height as oswego tea but it differs in having alternate lanceolate leaves. The flowers form a large terminal raceme one foot or more in length. Each flower, several inches in length, has a five-toothed green calyx and two-lipped corolla. The erect upper lip is divided into two lobes, and the lower lip has three narrow spreading segments. This orchidlike flower can be found from Canada to the Gulf of Mexico, and also in Southern California. It flowers from July through September.

Blue or Purple Flowers

A great number of the plants we find in swampy habitats have blue, purple, or lavender flowers. They vary in size from a fraction of an inch to more than one inch. Those with minute perianths, a quarter-inch or less in diameter, include forget-me-not, wild mint, marsh milkwort, and joe-pye weed. Those with larger flowers, a half inch or more in size, include swamp loosestrife, purple loosestrife, baby blue-eyes, shooting star, monkey flower, marsh blue violet, hooded skullcap, and purple fringed orchid.

Stream margins and wet shaded meadows are often tinted a delicate blue by the FORGET-ME-NOT which thrives in such habitats. This is a low-growing plant, a foot or two in height, with a tangle of slender, weak stems and lanceolate entire leaves. The flowers are borne in open, curving, one-sided racemes. Each flower has a five-lobed green calyx and a regular corolla of five small rounded petals, sky-blue and spotted with yellow at the base. Forget-me-not is common throughout the eastern United States, flowering from spring through summer. Several other species occur in North America, some with white as well as blue flowers.

WILD MINT is an aromatic plant of moist woods and stream margins, with square stems one to two feet in height. The oblong leaves grow opposite each other, the upper leaf pairs bearing small whorls of lavender or lilac-blue flowers. Each small flower is irregular, with a two-lipped corolla; the lower lip consists of three equal lobes, the upper lip is notched. Varieties with white or pinkish flowers are often found. Wild mint is a member of swamp

Some Blue or Purple Swamp Flowers: Forget-me-not (1);
Marsh Blue Violet (2); *Purple Loosestrife* (3); *Shooting Star*
(4); *Purple-fringed Orchid* (5); *Joe-pye Weed* (6); *Monkey
Flower* (7); *Hoooded Skullcap* (8).

communities from Canada to the Mississippi River Valley; it flowers from summer into autumn.

MARSH MILKWORT, also known as drumheads, is a plant of boggy meadows and wet pinelands of the eastern United States. The square stems, often growing to a height of two feet, bear simple linear leaves in whorls of four. Small purplish flowers are crowded into a spikelike raceme. Each flower has an irregular perianth, with a calyx of five sepals, two of which are winged and resemble petals, and a corolla of five petals, one forming a keel to the flower. Other species of milkwort have greenish or white flowers. Marsh milkwort flowers during summer and early autumn.

JOE-PYE WEED, or purple boneset, is a tall rank-growing plant of wet fields and roadside ditches, and it often reaches a height of six feet. Coarsely veined and wrinkled leaves, up to twelve inches in length, grow in whorls of three or more. Like boneset, which is a close relative, joe-pye weed is a composite. Therefore the tiny purple flowers are grouped in heads, which in turn form spreading flat-topped clusters. Each flower consists of a tubular corolla with five triangular lobes. Joe-pye weed is a common summer flower throughout the eastern half of the United States.

The remaining blue or purple flowers are larger and have more conspicuous perianths. Four of these have regular corollas: swamp loosestrife, purple loosestrife, baby blue-eyes, and shooting star. SWAMP LOOSESTRIFE is an angular-stemmed plant growing to a height of six to seven feet, with willowlike lanceolate leaves in pairs or whorls of three. Showy flowers form clusters in the axils of the upper leaf whorls. Each flower, about one inch in

80

length, has a regular corolla of six purple petals, with conspicuous projecting stamens, seated in a tubular calyx with a toothed margin. Swamp loosestrife grows in the eastern and southern United States, flowering during the summer.

PURPLE LOOSESTRIFE is a stiffly erect swamp dweller with square stems, growing to a height of six feet, which bear lanceolate simple leaves in pairs or whorls. The flowers form a dense terminal spike, thus differing from the inflorescence of swamp loosestrife. The individual flowers have a toothed green calyx and a regular corolla of shorter and more rounded petals than those of swamp loosestrife. This wild flower of the eastern United States also flowers during the summer.

BABY BLUE-EYES is a western member of the moist woods community, being found on the grassy slopes of California. It is a low-growing and spreading plant with opposite pinnately compound leaves and with flowers one-half inch in diameter growing in the leaf axils. Each flower has a green calyx with reflexed appendages, and a regular five-lobed corolla. This spring wild flower of the Southwest often shades into purple; a white-flowered relative lives in the moist woodlands of the southern United States.

SHOOTING STAR is another member of the western community, with relatives in the southeastern states; it thrives in wet meadows and canyon slopes, flowering during early summer. It is appropriately named, for the five reflexed petals of the regular corolla give a streamlined appearance, suggesting a falling star with a trail behind it. The delicately tinted lavender flowers, one-half to three-quarters of an inch in length, hang by long stalks in small

81

terminal clusters. The entire plant is rarely more than a foot in height, the slender stems arising from a basal rosette of oval, entire leaves.

Other blue or purple flowers with large perianths have irregular corollas; typical of these are blue violet, monkey flower, skullcap, and purple fringed orchid. MARSH BLUE VIOLET is the commonest of these irregular blue flowers of hydrophytic communities; this is a stemless violet with cordate or kidney-shaped leaves whose margins often curl inward. It prefers to grow in wet meadows and along marshy stream margins. Long slender flower stalks bear solitary deep-blue flowers of typical violet symmetry, with one of the five petals forming a backward-pointing spur. Marsh blue violet is a spring and summer wild flower found throughout the eastern half of the United States.

SQUARE-STEMMED MONKEY FLOWER, as the name indicates, is a square-stemmed plant; it bears lanceolate toothed leaves in pairs, and rarely grows more than a foot in height. Monkey flower has a distinct preference for gravelly pond shores, where it can be found, flowering from June to September, from Canada to the Gulf of Mexico. Solitary long-stemmed flowers grow in the upper leaf axils; each flower, about one inch in length, has a five-lobed green calyx and an irregular two-lipped corolla. The upper lip is reflexed, the lower spreading, somewhat resembling an animal's face. A western relative of the same name has bright yellow flowers.

HOODED SKULLCAP, a member of the Mint family, can be recognized by the irregular blue flowers about one inch in length, produced in pairs in the upper leaf axils. Skullcap, growing to a height of several feet, has opposite,

82

broadly lanceolate leaves. The corolla forms an elongated and curved tube with dilated throat; terminating the tubular portion are two lips, the lower lip being longer and more spreading than the upper. The common color is violet-blue, shading to white in the throat and tube; varieties with rose or white flowers can also be found. Hooded skullcap grows on sandy and gravelly shores, and in wet meadows edging the woods. It is found throughout North America, flowering all summer.

PURPLE FRINGED ORCHID is a lilac-purple wild flower of secluded damp woods in the cooler portions of the northern United States and Canada. A slender stem, growing to three feet in height, bears large alternate oval or lanceolate leaves. The flowers of this rare orchid are very fragrant, often being discovered by their pleasing scent before they can be seen. Each irregular corolla has a three-parted and spreading lower lip which is delicately fringed. The flowers are clustered in a spirelike raceme that grows to a length of seven or eight inches. Purple fringed orchid can be found in flower during July and August.

The Insect-Eating Wild Flowers

One of the thrills in exploring swamps or wet woods is the chance of finding the several kinds of strange carnivorous plants that trap and eat ants, flies, and other small animals. These are interesting more for their unusual leaves than for their flowers, since it is the modified leaves that catch such prey. Carnivorous plants are green and thus

can carry on photosynthesis. But, as we have learned earlier, they live in habitats which often are deficient in nitrogen, so the plants obtain this necessary element from the
organic remains of their captured animals. Three kinds of
carnivorous plants are found in North America: pitcher
plant, sundew, and Venus'-fly-trap.

PITCHER PLANT, also known as trumpets and frog

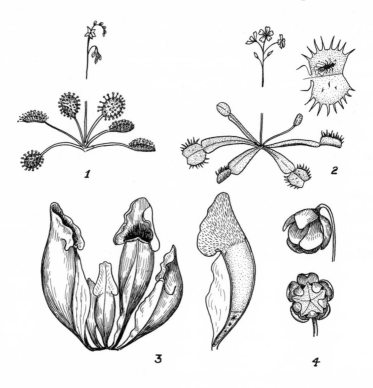

The Insectivorous Wild Flowers: Sundew (1); *Venus'-fly-trap*
(2) *with enlarged terminal portion of the leaf trap; Pitcher
Plant* (3) *with section view of a single hollow leaf, and flowers*
(4) *showing large pentagonal stigma.*

bonnet, is a low-growing plant, six to twelve inches tall, with a cluster of basal leaves whose blades are modified into upright pitchers or vases. Each modified leaf is green, mottled or striped with purple and brown. In some species the tip arches over the opening of the pitcher. Nectar-secreting cells located around the mouth of the pitcher produce the bait that attracts unsuspecting insects. The inside of the pitcher is armed with downward-pointing spines that facilitate the descent of the insect but prevent its escape. A pool of rainwater has usually collected in the bottom of the pitcher; in this the struggling insect eventually drowns. Then the body is digested by a secretion produced by the cells lining the pitcher, and the remains are absorbed into the leaf. Various kinds of pitcher plants are found in both the eastern and western United States. The flowers, which appear in summer, are regular, with five purplish sepals and five brown petals; an enlarged and flat-topped stigma forms a conspicuous structure in the center of the perianth. Each flower is nodding, borne on a long flower stalk; the flowers appear in early summer.

SUNDEW is a smaller plant, also found in low, wet ground and common in swamps and bogs throughout North America. Flattened, round leaf blades, each about the size of a small coin, form a basal rosette close to the ground; each leaf has a reddish tinge caused by the red-stalked glands that arise on the upper leaf surface like pins in a pincushion. The tips of these glandular hairs are sticky and give a glistening, dewy appearance to the plant. Each leaf, in spite of its attractiveness, can be a fatal trap for any wandering insect; such prey becomes entangled with the hairs and finds escape difficult. As it struggles to free itself, neighboring hairs actually bend over and help to pin it down. After the insect dies, its remains are digested and absorbed into the leaf as is the procedure in all carnivorous plants. Slender flower stalks, six to eight inches tall, bear small white or pink regular flowers in one-sided racemes. Each flower has four to eight sepals, and an equal number of separate petals; the flowers appear in summer.

VENUS'-FLY-TRAP is the most active and dramatic of all the insect-eating wild flowers; its range is more restricted, being found only in bogs and wet pinelands of North and South Carolina. The leaves form a basal rosette, close to the ground as in sundew. Each leaf is actually a complex mechanical trap, two to five inches in length. The blade is modified into two parts. The basal portion is narrow and functions as an ordinary green leaf; it then broadens out to form a wider terminal portion that is hinged along the midrib and has a margin armed with large teeth. The hinged midrib enables the blade to close, bringing the toothed margins together so that they eventually interlock. The middle of the leaf bears triggerlike hairs. When a fly or ant alights on the leaf and touches one of these triggers, the leaf folds along the midrib and the insect finds itself imprisoned. The pressure of the closed leaf blades is sufficient to crush soft-bodied insects. The closing of this plant trap takes only a few seconds; it then remains closed for a week or two during which the prey dies, is digested and absorbed. After that the Venus's-fly-trap opens again and is ready for another victim. Erect flower stalks, about one foot in height, bear clusters of small white flowers with a regular perianth of five sepals and five petals; the flowers appear in spring.

HOW TO IDENTIFY SOME SWAMP WILD FLOWERS

Clue No. 1. What is the color of the flower or its accessory parts?

If it is green or brown, go to Clue No. 2.

If it is white, go to Clue No. 4.

If it is yellow or orange, go to Clue No. 11.

If it is red or pink, go to Clue No. 16.

If it is blue, purple, or lavender go to Clue No. 19.

Clue No. 2. What is the type of inflorescence?

If the flowers are in a spreading panicle .... AMERICAN HELLEBORE.

If the flowers are in a terminal spike ... LEAFY GREEN ORCHIS.

If the flowers are on a spadix, surrounded by a spathe, go to Clue No. 3.

Clue No. 3. What is the shape of the spathe?

If a conical hood, hiding completely the spadix .... SKUNK CABBAGE.

If cylindrical, open at top revealing spadix .... JACK-IN-THE-PULPIT.

Clue No. 4. What is the size of the flower?

If ¼ inch or less, go to Clue No. 5.

If ½ inch or more, go to Clue No. 7.

Clue No. 5. What is the type of inflorescence?

If the flowers are in a spreading panicle .... MEADOW RUE.

If the flowers are in a braided spike .... LADIES' TRESSES.

If the flowers are in a head (composite) .... BONESET.

If the flowers are in an umbel go to Clue No. 6.

Clue No. 6. What is the nature of the stems?

If corrugated and green .... WATER PARSNIP.

If spotted and smooth .... SPOTTED COWBANE.

Clue No. 7. What type of symmetry does the flower have?

If the corolla is regular, go to Clue No. 8.

If the corolla is irregular, go to Clue No. 9.

Clue No. 8. Does the corolla have a central accessory structure?

If the stamen stalks form a saucerlike structure .. SPIDER LILY.

If no such structure is present .... CRINUM LILY.

87

Clue No. 9. How are the flowers arranged on the plant?

If the flowers are solitary, go to Clue No. 10.
If the flowers are in a spike .... TURTLEHEAD.

Clue No. 10. What is the nature of the corolla?

If one petal forms an inflated sac .... SHOWY LADY'S SLIPPER.
If one petal forms a spur .... WATER VIOLET.

Clue No. 11. How large is the flower?

If ½ inch or less, go to Clue No. 12.
If ¾ inch or more, go to Clue No. 14.

Clue No. 12. What type of symmetry does the flower have?

If irregular .... ORANGE MILKWORT.
If regular, go to Clue No. 13.

Clue No. 13. How are the flowers arranged on the stem?

If the flowers are in terminal spikes .... SWAMP CANDLES.
If in axillary clusters .... WHORLED LOOSESTRIFE.

Clue No. 14. What type of symmetry does the flower have?

If it is regular .... MARSH MARIGOLD.
If it is irregular, go to Clue No. 15.

Clue No. 15. How large are the flowers?

If less than 2 inches in length .... TOUCH-ME-NOT.
If more than 2 inches in length .... GOLDEN CANNA.

Clue No. 16. What type of symmetry does the flower have?

If it is regular, go to Clue No. 17.
If it is irregular, go to Clue No. 18.

Clue No. 17. Where are the anthers of the stamens located?

If present at the summit of the stamen column ....
.... MARSHMALLOW.
If absent from the summit of the stamen column ....
.... SWAMP ROSE MALLOW.

Clue No. 18. What type of inflorescence does the plant have?

If a rounded cluster, seated in red bracts ...... OSWEGO TEA.
If spikelike, without red bracts .... CARDINAL FLOWER.

Clue No. 19. How large are the flowers?

If ¼ inch or less go to Clue No. 20.
If ½ inch or larger go to Clue No. 21.

Clue No. 20. What is the type of inflorescence?

If the flowers are in axillary whorls .... WILD MINT.

If the flowers are in open racemes .... FORGET-ME-NOT.

If the flowers are in spikes .... MARSH MILKWORT.

If the flowers are in heads (composite) ...... JOE-PYE WEED.

Clue No. 21. What type of symmetry does the flower have?

If regular, go to Clue No. 22.

If irregular, go to Clue No. 23.

Clue No. 22. How are the flowers arranged on the stem?

If solitary, in leaf axils (western U.S. only) .. BABY BLUE-EYES.

If nodding, in umbels (western and central U.S.) ....
.... SHOOTING STAR.

If clustered in axils of leaves .... SWAMP LOOSESTRIFE.

If in a spike .... PURPLE LOOSESTRIFE.

Clue No. 23. How are the flowers arranged on the stem?

If solitary, close to the ground .... MARSH BLUE VIOLET.

If in spikelike terminal racemes .... PURPLE FRINGED ORCHID.

If in the leaf axils, go to Clue No. 24.

Clue No. 24. What is the shape of the corolla?

If the upper lip is helmet-shaped ....HOODED SKULLCAP.

If upper lip is not helmet-shaped .... MONKEY FLOWER.

White trillium, like all trilliums, has its floral parts in threes: a calyx of three green sepals, a corolla of three white petals, six stamens, and a three-pronged style to the pistil.

CHAPTER FIVE

FLOWERS AT HOME
IN WOODS AND FORESTS

Woods and forests provide the type of environment suited for many small, delicate herbaceous plants which are mesophytes. Forest soil, since it retains rainfall for long periods, remains moderately moist throughout the year; yet it is rarely flooded to such an extent as to damage the wild flowers. Forest soil is also rich in humus from the annual accumulation of fallen leaves and twigs. There the sunlight is never intense, yet adequate for photosynthesis. Woodland shade reduces transpiration and thus conserves water within the plants. Small forest wild flowers, being sheltered by the shrubs and trees, are protected from damage by winds and storms. Mesophytes of these habitats include most of our early spring wild flowers. It is in the woods that we find such seasonal pioneers as hepatica, anemone, bloodroot, spring beauty, violet, and Canada mayflower. In fact, the great majority of eastern wildflowers of woods and forests appear between April and June; few can be found after midsummer.

Living conditions vary in minor details throughout wood and forest areas. The dense evergreen forests of northern North America provide a cooler home for a wild-flower community, though with a shorter growing season, than the open pinelands of the southeastern United States. The deciduous oak and maple forests of the central United States offer a second type of home, with different light and moisture conditions and milder temperatures. Open thickets and cutover forest regions provide still a third type of habitat with less mesophytic conditions. Some woodland flowers thrive in one habitat, some in another. Mingled with these mesophytes in low wet woods or swampy thickets may be some of the hydrophytes described in the previous chapter, especially blue flag, forget-me-not, skunk cabbage, and Jack-in-the-pulpit. On sandy and rocky slopes or ridges, where the lack of moisture is the greatest, we can find some of the xerophytic wild flowers introduced in the next chapter. The observant naturalist soon learns what special types of environment each species of wild flower prefers.

As we discovered in our exploration of hydrophytic communities, recognition of wild flowers becomes easier if we look for clues to their significant features. Woodland and forest flowers can also be grouped on the basis of color, even though a few species belong in several color categories. For flowers of the same color, other valuable clues are seen in the size of the perianth, its symmetry, and the type of inflorescence.

Green Woodland Flowers

Two common members of the woods community have inconspicuous greenish flowers. These are Indian cucumber root and hairy Solomon's seal. INDIAN CUCUMBER ROOT has its home in the moist shaded woods of eastern North America; its name comes from the cucumberlike flavor of the edible rootstock. This slender-stemmed plant, a foot or two in height, has simple oval leaves arranged in two whorls; a lower whorl of five or six leaves, and an upper whorl of three leaves. Above the upper whorl is borne a cluster of several nodding flowers, each one-half inch or less in diameter. Indian cucumber root is a member of the Lily family, and therefore has a regular perianth of six segments with no distinction between sepals and petals. The segments are recurved and surround a conspicuous projecting three-parted style. Indian cucumber root flow-

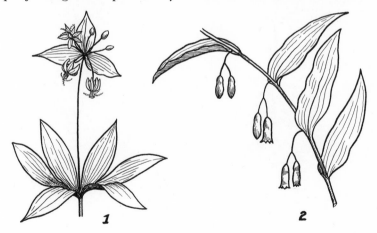

Some Green Woodland Flowers: Indian Cucumber Root (1)
and Hairy Solomon's Seal (2).

93

ers from March through June; in summer it bears dark blue berries.

HAIRY SOLOMON'S SEAL prefers more open, rocky woods and ridges; it, too, occurs throughout eastern North America. The name is derived from the scar, resembling a seal, left on the rhizome by last year's stem. Hairy Solomon's seal has slender, slightly zigzag stems growing to a height of twelve to eighteen inches and arching downward at the tip. The foliage consists of simple oval leaves with parallel venation growing opposite each other on the stem.

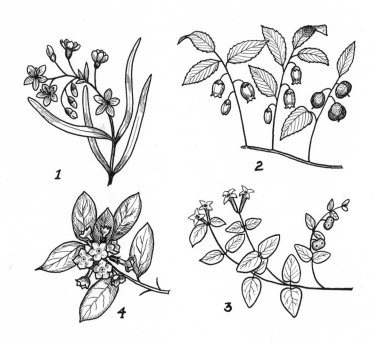

White Woodland Flowers with Trailing Habit: Spring Beauty (1); Checkerberry (2); Partridgeberry (3); Mayflower (4).

94

This wild flower is also a member of the Lily family; thus its flowers are regular, with a six-lobed margin. The flowers, about one-half inch in length, hang in pairs from the leaf axils; each flower looks as if it were in bud because the tubular perianth, constricted in the middle, has only a small opening at its tip, in the shape of a flower not yet open. Hairy Solomon's seal is in flower from March through June; in summer it develops dark blue berries.

White Woodland Flowers

A great number of the woods and forest plants have white flowers. Most of these are characterized by regular perianths, with the flowers borne solitary or in small clusters. They vary in their habit of growth, however. Some have strong stems that hold the plant erect. Others have weaker stems and grow close to the ground, trailing or climbing on other plants. Four members of the woodland community with white flowers have such a prostrate, trailing habit: spring beauty, checkerberry, partridgeberry, and mayflower.

SPRING BEAUTY is a plant of open woods and clearings where it forms a tangle of foliage and flowers rarely more than six inches in height, the flowers growing in spreading clusters. There are two common species of spring beauty: one has oval pointed leaves, the other has linear, grasslike leaves. Both occur in eastern woods. The flower is aptly named, for the regular corolla consists of five white petals, each delicately striped with pink. The flowers are about one-half inch in diameter. Spring beauty blooms from March through May.

CHECKERBERRY, or teaberry, is a creeping plant of dry open woods and thickets, found throughout the eastern United States; it is especially common beneath evergreen trees. Early settlers in New England brewed a tea from the foliage. Checkerberry has aromatic evergreen leaves, elliptic in shape. The urn-shaped regular flowers, less than one-half inch in diameter, are produced in the leaf axils, either solitary or in groups of two or three. The flowering branches usually arch upward. Each flower is nodding, with the fused petals forming a tubular corolla edged with five small lobes. Checkerberry is among the few members of the woods community that flower in summer. The fruit is a red, edible berry.

PARTRIDGEBERRY, a prostrate plant of moist shaded woods, ranges from Canada to Florida and west to Texas. The evergreen foliage consists of shiny small oval leaves which grow in pairs. Fragrant waxy-white flowers, one-half inch or less in size, also occur in pairs, united at the base. Each flower has a regular perianth, the petals being fused to form a funnel-shaped corolla with four recurved lobes. Partridgeberry, like checkerberry, flowers during the summer. After flowering, the ovaries of the flower pairs unite to form a single red berry, spicy and edible. Because the foliage is evergreen and the red berries remain on the plant all winter, partridgeberry is favored for use in terraria and miniature bowl gardens.

MAYFLOWER, also known as trailing arbutus, thrives on shaded, well drained banks and slopes at edges of woodlands. It is a creeping plant with oval evergreen leaves that have a rough leathery surface. Clusters of fragrant white flowers, each about half an inch in length, are hidden

96

Bunchberry (*left*) is a herbaceous cousin of the dogwood tree, and, like it, has conspicuous white bracts beneath clusters of small yellowish flowers. Mayflower (*right*) is an evergreen with fragrant white flowers, blooming early in spring.

among the foliage. Each flower has a regular, tubular corolla, often tinted with pink; the margin of the corolla is five-lobed. This prized member of the woods community flowers from March to May. Once abundant in the northeastern United States, mayflower is now rare in many areas because of careless picking and uprooting of the plants. It is one of the many unique wild flowers we will enjoy discovering, but should leave for others' pleasure also.

Of the white woodland flowers that have an erect habit of growth, some are very small while others are large and

97

showy. Representative of those with small flowers, one-half an inch in diameter or less, are bunchberry, Canada mayflower, false Solomon's seal, and camass. BUNCHBERRY, also called ground dogwood and dwarf cornel, is a herbaceous relative of the dogwood tree. This plant of Canada and our cooler northern states often forms a dense ground cover over large areas. Preferring habitats with some sunshine as well as shade, it is most frequently encountered in open forest glades and along wooded roads. A short erect stem, six inches or less in height, bears at its summit a whorl of five or six simple, ovate, pointed leaves. Above the leaf cluster rises a short flower stalk bearing four to six white bracts, each one inch or more in length; these bracts are likely to be mistaken for petals. However, the actual bunchberry flowers are small and yellowish green, with four minute petals; they form a spherical cluster above the petal-like bracts. Bunchberry is in flower from May to June; later the flowers are replaced by a cluster of bright red berries.

CANADA MAYFLOWER is another spring wild flower of cool woods and forests, abundant in Canada and northern New England. It has several other names, among them wild lily-of-the-valley and two-leaved Solomon's seal. Erect zigzag stems, three to six inches in height, bear several alternate oval leaves with the parallel venation typical of the Lily family, to which it belongs. The individual flowers, less than one-quarter of an inch in diameter, are borne in an elongated terminal raceme. Each flower has a perianth of four spreading segments. The flowers appear in May and June; in summer Canada mayflower produces speckled brown berries which become pale red when mature.

Canada mayflower, a diminutive member of the Lily family, has small white flowers in an elongated raceme on a zigzag stem, above two or three glossy green leaves.

Woodland Plants with Small White Flowers: Canada Mayflower (1); Bunchberry (2); False Solomon's Seal (3); Camass (4).

EARLY SAXIFRAGE, found in dry rocky woods throughout eastern North America, also flowers in spring, from April through May. Saxifrages—of which there are many different species—can be recognized by the basal cluster of ovate and toothed leaves, above which rises a flower stalk eight to ten inches in height. This is topped by a small cluster of white or greenish flowers, each only one-quarter of an inch in diameter. Each flower has a regular corolla of five separate oblong petals.

Of larger size and coarser growth habits is FALSE SOLOMON'S SEAL, which often forms extensive beds of white feathery flowers along wooded country roads. Several different species occur throughout North America. The erect zigzag stem grows to a height of three or four feet, bearing large oval alternate leaves which are conspicuously parallel-veined, a characteristic of many species in the Lily family, to which false Solomon's seal belongs. The flowers are borne in a large spreading panicle, a foot or more in length and terminating the leafy stem. Each flower, about one-quarter of an inch in size, has six spreading similar segments; the flowers appear in May and June. In late summer they are replaced by clusters of bright red berries.

Several kinds of camass occur in wooded habitats throughout the United States. Camass is a member of the Lily family with linear grasslike leaves which sprout from an onionlike bulb. WHITE CAMASS, a plant one to three feet in height, found from Canada to Virginia, prefers habitats with limestone soils. The flowers grow in an open cluster; each flower is creamy white, less than one-half an inch in diameter. The six spreading segments are tinged with green on the back. DEATH CAMASS, with similar foliage and habits, grows in more hydrophytic habitats, being found on moist wooded slopes of the western United States. Small white or greenish flowers, each with a regular six-parted perianth, are borne in large spreading panicles. Death camass is poisonous to grazing animals, especially sheep.

Some white flowers of woods and forests have larger, more showy perianths than the preceding species. A few of these produce solitary flowers, others bear the flowers in clusters. Representative of these members of the community are wood anemone, rue anemone, bloodroot, May apple, white trillium, and Atamasco lily. The flowers of others are in an inflorescence of the raceme or umbel type. Typical of these are wintergreen, shinleaf, pipsissewa, and woodland star.

WOOD ANEMONE, also known as windflower, prefers open sandy or rocky woods; it is often found in clearings and roadside thickets where more sunlight penetrates than in the deep woods. Wood anemone is a member of the Buttercup family found throughout eastern North America. This species has an erect stem, growing to a height of ten inches and terminating in a cluster of three compound leaves. Above the leaves rises a solitary flower, growing to an inch in diameter. Wood anemone has a perianth of five white sepals, but no petals.

RUE ANEMONE grows in the open woods of eastern North America. It is a delicate-stemmed plant which reaches a height of seven or eight inches. The leaves are compound, consisting of small lobed leaflets; some leaves are basal, others form a cluster beneath the flowers. The

101

flowers are white or pinkish, about one-half inch in diameter, and borne in a small cluster above the leaves. Rue anemone is also a member of the Buttercup family, and like many other wild flowers in this family has a regular perianth of five to ten colored sepals, but no petals. Rue anemone can be found in flower from March through June.

BLOODROOT, growing throughout eastern North America, often forms beds of snowy-white flowers at the edges of thickets in rich open woods. Being a member of the Poppy family, it has the colored sap characteristic of poppy species. The common name refers to the orange-red sap of the stem and rootstock, which also contain a poisonous compound. A single large palmately lobed leaf rises from the ground on a long petiole; frequently the leaf is

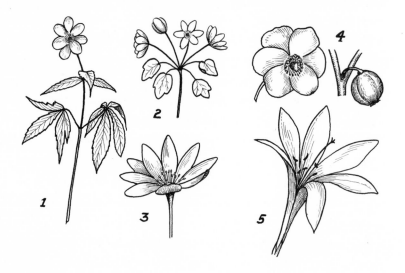

Woodland Plants with Large White Flowers: Wood Anemone (1); *Rue Anemone* (2); *Bloodroot* (3); *May Apple, flower and fruit* (4); *Atamasco Lily* (5).

Bloodroot (*left*) a member of the Poppy family, gets its name from the orange-red sap of roots and stem. Hepatica (*right*), a member of the Buttercup family, has colored sepals which may be white, lavender or blue.

coiled around the flower stalk with its solitary terminal flower. Each flower, growing to an inch in diameter, has two short-lived sepals and eight to ten long narrow petals. Bloodroot flowers appear in March and continue to bloom through May; the fruit is a narrow and pointed capsule.

MAY APPLE, so named because of the edible yellow berry which appears on the plant in early summer, is found in open deciduous woods of the eastern United States. This wild flower is another gregarious member of the woodland community, often forming extensive colonies on moist slopes. May apple has unusual large-lobed leaves, supported in a horizontal position by an unbranched stem; this distinctive foliage is responsible for another common

103

name, umbrella-leaf. Still another name for this plant is mandrake, in reference to its poisonous rootstock. In flowering individuals the stem forks into two petioles, each bearing one large umbrellalike leaf. At the angle between the two petioles is a single large nodding white flower, one or more inches in diameter. Each flower has a regular perianth of six to nine broad petals. The flowers appear in April and May.

WHITE TRILLIUM, like the trilliums we encountered in the swamp community, can be recognized by the arrangement of the leaves and flower parts in threes. This species prefers the moist open woods and sparse thickets of the northeastern United States. White trillium has an unbranched erect stem growing to a height of ten inches; the top of the stem bears three large ovate leaves with pointed tips. Above the leaves is a large solitary flower, several inches in diameter. Each flower has three green pointed sepals and three broader white petals. White trillium is in flower from April through June; it develops a blue-black berry in summer. PAINTED TRILLIUM, of the same size and general appearance, has somewhat stouter stems and bluish-green leaves. This trillium inhabits the cool woods of the northeastern United States and Canada. Each flower consists of three small green sepals and three larger wavy-margined petals which are white, veined with magenta. Painted trillium is a colorful wild flower, found from April to June; its fruit is a bright red berry.

If we leave the cool forests of the northern United States for the warmer deciduous woods of the southeastern portion of the country, we will discover ATAMASCO LILY, a

Atamasco lily, of moist fields in the southeastern United States, bears vase-shaped flowers which seem to spring directly out of the ground.

member of the Amaryllis family, which thrives in moist, grassy, open woods; it also adapts itself to fields and road-sides that are amply supplied with water. This lilylike plant is stemless, a few grasslike leaves growing directly from the underground bulb. An erect flower stalk, six to eight inches in height, bears a solitary funnel-shaped flower several inches in length. Atamasco lily is a showy wild flower with a perianth of six segments, alike in color. The lower portion of the sepals and petals is fused to form a tubular base. Atamasco lilies appear in April and con-tinue to bloom until June. Seminole Indians made a con-coction from the bulbs for use as a toothache medicine.

The three remaining white flowers we will meet are members of the northern forest community and are all species of the Heath family, with similar growth habits and flower design: pipsissewa, wintergreen, and shinleaf. PIPSISSEWA, also known as prince's pine, is a low-growing evergreen plant of dry woods, especially common under conifer trees; it is found in the Rocky Mountains as well as in the eastern United States. Short erect stems, reaching a height of six inches, bear narrow, wedge-shaped and toothed leaves. A few white or pink flowers are borne in a small umbel at the tip of the flower stalk. Each flower, about one-half an inch in diameter, has a regular corolla of five separate concave petals; the base of the corolla is generally marked by a deep pink ring. A stout pistil with

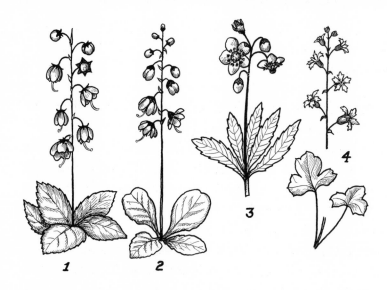

Woodland White Flowers in Inflorescences: Wintergreen (1); *Shinleaf* (2); *Pipsissewa* (3); *Woodland Star* (4).

106

a conspicuous globular stigma projects beyond the corolla. Pipsissewa is in flower during July and August.

ROUND-LEAVED WINTERGREEN inhabits dry sandy woods from Nova Scotia southward through the eastern United States; it is well known for its aromatic and spicy foliage. Round-leaved wintergreen is a low-growing plant with a basal cluster of oval, toothed leaves, which like those of pipsissewa are evergreen. A slender flower stalk, twelve inches or more in height, terminates in an erect raceme of nodding white or pink flowers that are very fragrant. Each flower, about one-half inch in diameter, has a regular corolla of five concave, thick, rounded petals. An upward curving style projects conspicuously beyond the corolla. Round-leaved wintergreen flowers from June to August.

SHINLEAF, also called wild lily-of-the-valley, is very similar to round-leaved wintergreen, but its elliptic leaves are a lighter green and deciduous, not evergreen. The leaves form a basal cluster from which rises the flower stalk, terminated by a raceme of nodding, fragrant white flowers. The regular corolla consists of five concave petals, beyond which projects the curved style. Shinleaf is found in the rich dry woods of southern Canada and the eastern United States; it is in flower during July and August.

If our explorations take us to the western United States, the white-flowered WOODLAND STAR will be found frequently on wooded slopes in the forests of the Pacific coast. A relative of saxifrage, woodland star has a similar basal cluster of leaves which, in this species, are rounded and three-lobed. An erect flower stalk, about twelve inches high, terminates in a loose raceme of flowers, each about

107

one-half inch in diameter. The flowers have a regular perianth of five petals with three-lobed tips.

Yellow Woodland Flowers

The yellow woodland flowers can be identified on the basis
of the presence or absence of an inflorescence and its type,
if present. In one group the flowers are solitary or borne in
a small indefinite cluster, some terminal and some in the
axils of the leaves. Representative of these members of the
woods-and-forest community are yellow violet, dogtooth
violet, dogberry, bellwort, and yellow lady's slipper. In another group the plants have many small flowers arranged
in a spike, raceme, or head. Typical of these are wood
betony, Dutchman's breeches, and cup plant.

Yellow Woodland Flowers: Dogtooth Violet (1); *Dogberry* (2);
Bellwort (3); *Yellow Lady's Slipper* (4).

108

YELLOW VIOLET is a species of violet growing on moist wooded slopes and in the partial shade of deciduous trees of eastern North America; it is in flower during April and May. Yellow violet is a leafy-stemmed plant with ovate or kidney-shaped leaves borne on long petioles and reaching a height of six to eight inches. The flowers, with the irregular, spurred corolla typical of all violets, grow in axillary clusters. Each flower, one-half an inch in length, has petals that are brownish purple in some individuals, as well as yellow. A western yellow violet of the same habit and size, but with cordate and palmately lobed leaves, grows in the mountain forests of the Pacific coast.

DOGTOOTH VIOLET is called by a number of other names, among them yellow adder's-tongue and trout lily. Found throughout eastern North America, it frequently forms extensive wild-flower gardens in moist grassy habitats along the edge of open woods; it is more venturesome than most woodland flowers and as a result is often found in open fields. Other species with white, pink, or purplish flowers occur in the central United States. Dogtooth violet is a stemless plant, the erect lanceolate leaves rising directly from the ground. The leaves, a distinctively mottled green and brown, sheath erect flower stalks eight to ten inches tall. This wild flower is a member of the Lily family, and thus has a perianth of six segments, with sepals and petals alike in size and color. The nodding flower has inch-long segments that form a narrow, bell-shaped perianth. The pale yellow flowers merge inconspicuously into the surrounding vegetation. Dogtooth violet blooms from early April into June.

DOGBERRY, or yellow Clintonia, another woodland

member of the Lily family, lives in the rich moist woods of our northern states and Canada. Large oval leaves with parallel venation form a basal cluster from which rises a leafless flower stalk one foot or more in height. This terminates in an umbel of three to six flowers, each less than one-half an inch in diameter, with a regular perianth of six segments; petals and sepals are both a yellowish green. The narrow segments of the flower surround conspicuous projecting stamens and pistil. This early spring wild flower blossoms from May into June. In summer the plants bear shiny blue berries. A species with smaller white flowers and black berries is found in the southern states.

BELLWORT, also in the Lily family, is at home in the rich moist woods of eastern North America. The slender forking stem, growing to a height of twenty inches, bears oval leaves with parallel venation; the base of each leaf surrounds the stem in a characteristic clasping fashion. The stem terminates in drooping flowers with a pale-yellow, bell-shaped perianth of six segments, sepals and petals alike in appearance. Bellwort is another early spring wild flower, blooming in April and May. A related species known as WILD OATS has similar pale-yellow drooping flowers, but the leaves are sessile and do not clasp the stem. It lives in the same type of habitat as bellwort, throughout the northeastern United States.

YELLOW LADY'S SLIPPER, also known as downy lady's slipper, is an orchid of moist habitats in the cool woods of the northern United States. This species grows to a height of twelve inches; the stems bear large oval pointed leaves. A tall flower stalk terminates in a nodding flower with the large irregular corolla typical of lady's slippers.

The three sepals are twisted and purplish; two of the petals are an inconspicuous purplish brown, but the third petal, shaped like an inflated sac one inch or more in length, is yellow. Yellow lady's slipper can be found in flower from April into June.

In the shaded canyons of the California Sierras grows a stately member of the Lily family, the HUMBOLDT LILY. This is a wild flower three to six feet tall, with the erect stems bearing whorls of lanceolate leaves. Small clusters of orange-red, nodding flowers terminate the stem. The showy flowers, up to five inches in diameter, consist of six recurved segments spotted with purplish brown;

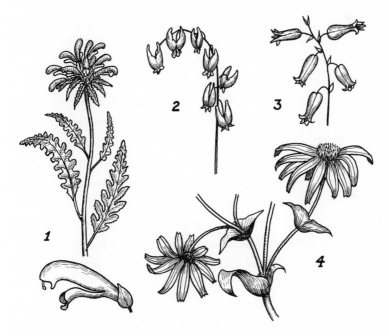

Yellow Woodland Flowers: Wood Betony (1); *Dutchman's Breeches* (2); *Squirrel Corn* (3); *Cup Plant* (4).

111

sepals and petals are alike in color and shape. This western lily is in bloom from June to August.

The preceding yellow woodland flowers grow singly or in small clusters. The following species in this color category have the flowers arranged in a definite inflorescence. WOOD BETONY is a wild flower of the open woods and thickets of eastern North America, often found along the wooded margin of fields. It is a low-growing plant, less than twelve inches tall; its fernlike, pinnately lobed leaves form a dense mass surrounding the flowers borne in a compact terminal spike, intermingled with leafy bracts. Each flower, about one inch in length, has a yellowish-brown irregular corolla which is conspicuously two-lipped. The beaklike upper lip arches over the crested and three-lobed lower one. Wood betony can be found in flower from April to June.

DUTCHMAN'S BREECHES is another low-growing, tufted member of the rich woods community of the eastern United States. Fernlike compound leaves with finely divided leaflets form a basal cluster from which rise elongated racemes of pendant yellow and white flowers. Each flower has an irregular corolla, about one-half inch in length, which resembles an inverted pair of baggy trousers. The corolla consists of two pairs of petals; the outermost pair has conspicuous divergent spurs (forming the "breeches"), the inner pair is narrow and crested. Dutchman's breeches is in flower during April and May. A relative, known as SQUIRREL CORN, is very similar in appearance; however, the flowers are greenish-white tinted with rose, and the short spurs do not diverge as in Dutchman's breeches. The common name refers to the small cornlike tubers growing along the underground stem.

112

CUP PLANT is one of the few wild flowers of the Composite family which is a member of the woodland community. It lives in damp habitats on wooded river banks and on moist slopes of the central United States. Cup plant is a rank-growing, square-stemmed plant six or seven feet tall with simple, coarsely toothed leaves opposite each other on the stem. The common name refers to the unique cuplike structure formed where the leaf bases surround the stem. Numerous small flowers are crowded into a large head several inches in diameter. The margin of the head consists of narrow yellow ray flowers; the central disk is made up of yellow tubular flowers. Cup plant is in flower during July and August.

Red or Pink Woodland Flowers

Six common red woodland flowers are members of the Lily family, with the characteristic perianth of segments in threes and sixes. These are red trillium, twisted stalk, wood lily, leopard lily, Carolina lily, and Turk's-cap lily. Other flowers of woods and forests with red or pinkish corollas include columbine, moss pink, and centaury. Among the irregular flowers are scarlet larkspur and moccasin flower.

RED TRILLIUM, also known as wake-robin and birthwort, is an unpleasantly scented wild flower of rich woods in the northeastern United States. Like the other species of trillium we have met, its leaves, petals, and sepals occur in groups of three. An unbranched erect stem grows to a height of twelve inches; at its tip is a whorl of three large ovate leaves, and above them a solitary flower one inch or slightly more in diameter. The sepals are brown and

Red or Pink Woodland Flowers: Turk's-cap Lily (1); *Leopard Lily* (2); *Wood Lily* (3); *Red Trillium* (4); *Columbine* (5); *Moss Pink* (6); *Scarlet Larkspur* (7); *Moccasin Flower* (8); *Centaury* (9).

Twisted stalk, of shaded woodland communities, has rose-purple flowers which hang like small bells from the leaf axils.

pointed, the petals are broader and a maroon red. Red trillium flowers in April and continues in bloom through May; in summer the plant bears a single large red berry. Several other species of reddish-brown trilliums are found in the central and southern United States.

TWISTED STALK is another wild flower of the rich, shaded, woodland community in the northeastern United States. The zigzag stem, several feet in height, bears alternate oval leaves, conspicuously parallel-veined. Delicate rose-purple flowers, one-half inch or less in length, hang from the leaf axils; the perianth is bell-shaped with six spreading recurved segments. Twisted stalk can be found in flower from May through June. The fruit, developing in late summer, is a bright red berry.

115

WOOD LILY, also known as wild red lily, is an orange-red flower of dry woods and open thickets where it is exposed to some sunshine during the day; its range is eastern Canada and the northeastern United States. Stiffly erect stems grow to a height of several feet, bearing whorls of three or more slender lanceolate leaves. At the top of the stem develops a single flower, or a group of several flowers; each flower is three or four inches in length. The vase-shaped perianth consists of six spreading segments, each with a narrowed basal portion; the segments are alike, with purplish spots on the reddish-orange background. Wood lilies flower during July and August.

TURK'S-CAP LILY is a taller plant, five or six feet in height, found in low wet woods throughout eastern North America. Erect stems bear lanceolate leaves which occur in whorls on the lower portion of the stem in pairs near its tip. Nodding, orange-scarlet flowers grow singly or in small clusters. Each flower has six slender recurved segments spotted with purple at the base and with no distinction between sepals and petals. Turk's-cap lilies are in flower from July until early September.

Southeastern woodland communities include two additional species of lily. LEOPARD LILY, or southern red lily, grows in roadside thickets from the Carolinas southward. Its slender stems rarely grow more than two feet in height; they bear erect orange-red flowers similar to the northern wood lily. The flowers are solitary or in small clusters, each flower three inches in diameter with rounded perianth segments tapering to a slender base. It blossoms from June to July. CAROLINA LILY or southern swamp lily, is also the same color as the northern wood lily, with

Columbine, with species found in almost every state, and in red, white and blue colors, could well be called our national wild flower.

similar whorls of leaves; the leaves, however, have a whitish bloom in contrast to the bright green of the leopard lily. The flowers are usually nodding rather than erect. Carolina lilies thrive in oak and pine woods from Virginia southward.

COLUMBINE, or rock bells, is an unusually attractive wild flower of the rocky slopes and ledges in the open woods of the northeastern United States. Erect slender stems, forming branching plants, grow to a height of several feet; they bear compound leaves divided into many small rounded and lobed leaflets. Pendant scarlet flowers, an inch or more in length, develop at the tips of the stems. The perianth consists of ten colored segments, both sepals

117

and petals being red; the petals, however, project backward into long conical spurs, and the sepals extend outward between the petals. Yellow stamens hang beneath the perianth like tiny clappers on a bell. Columbine is the showiest wild-flower member of the Buttercup family and is found in flower during April and May. A number of other species of columbine, some with white, others with blue or yellow flowers, occurs throughout North America from Alaska to Mexico. Since it is found in so many of our states, and includes red, white, and blue color variations, columbine could appropriately be selected as a national flower.

MOSS PINK, a low trailing plant of the sunny open woods, thrives in sandy well drained soils throughout the eastern United States. It has a partially woody stem and semievergreen linear leaves. It is one of many species in the Phlox family, which also includes numerous garden species used as rock plants. Phlox flowers have a regular perianth with a five-lobed calyx and a tubular five-lobed corolla. In moss pink the upward arching tips of the stems produce clusters of pink flowers, each about one-half an inch in diameter; the petals have distinctive notched tips. Moss pink flowers from April through May. Another species, HAIRY PHLOX, is a tufted plant with opposite lanceolate leaves and clusters of rose-pink or violet flowers. A characteristic feature is the hairy stem. This species prefers open sandy woods and edges of meadows; it is most abundant in the southern United States. Hairy phlox is in flower from May to July.

CENTAURY is an erect plant, several feet in height, growing in partial shade in woods and meadows; one species occurs in the southern United States, another amid shrubs on the Pacific coast. The stems bear linear opposite leaves and rose-colored or pink flowers in terminal spikes or spreading clusters. Centaury is a relative of the gentians, and has the same regular perianth with a four- or five-parted calyx; the corolla is saucer-shaped with a tubular base formed by the fusion of the petals. The margin of the corolla has five spreading segments. Centaury is in flower from late spring to early summer.

MOCCASIN FLOWER, or pink lady's slipper, is an orchid of open, often sandy woods of the eastern United States. It is a stemless plant with several large oval basal leaves with the parallel venation typical of many orchids. An erect leafless flower stalk grows to a height of ten or twelve inches, terminating in a solitary drooping flower. The three sepals are yellowish green, often tinged with purple. One of the three petals forms the enlarged and saclike lip, rosy pink in color and marked with a pattern of red veins. Moccasin flower can be found in bloom during spring from early April into May.

SCARLET LARKSPUR, a vividly colored wild flower of southern California, prefers a home beneath the shrubs and trees on the lower slopes of mountains. It grows to a height of three or four feet. Scarlet larkspur belongs to a group of species in the Buttercup family with irregular flowers; it has the palmately compound leaves with five- to seven-lobed leaflets typical of the family. Like its garden relatives, this larkspur develops its flowers in a tapering terminal raceme. The perianth has a scarlet calyx with one of the five sepals prolonged into a spur; the posterior pair of colored petals is also spurred.

Blue or Purple Woodland Flowers

Many of the blue or purple woodland flowers of the eastern United States form communities in moist habitats such as shaded woods, banks of streams, and wet wooded meadows. Here we can find wild geranium, herb Robert, fringed and bottle gentians, spiderwort, scorpionweed, and blue violet. In dry rocky woods grows wild blue phlox. If our woodland explorations take us to the central and western states, we find such additions to the community as dwarf larkspur, blue-eyed Mary, and Chinese houses.

WILD GERANIUM, also known as spotted crane's-bill, is an erect wild flower with slender branching stems and palmately lobed leaves; it grows to a height of twenty inches. The delicately tinted, rose-purple or lavender flowers, about one inch in diameter, occur in small terminal clusters. Each flower has a regular perianth with a calyx of five green sepals and a corolla of five separate petals. Wild geranium flowers from April to June, and extends over a wide range in the eastern United States. The elongated and sharply tipped fruit capsule resembles the outstretched head and bill of a crane. This capsule demonstrates a unique method of seed dispersal. Sections of the capsule split open lengthwise and, as the segments uncoil, they catapult the seeds outward.

HERB ROBERT, found in wooded ravines and rocky openings of forests in northeastern North America, is a relative of wild geranium with somewhat similar appearance. The individual flowers, however, are much smaller, usually less than half an inch in diameter, and the foliage is more fernlike, being pinnately lobed and strongly

120

Blue or Purple Woodland Flowers: Herb Robert (1); Wild Geranium (2); Scorpionweed (3); Spiderwort (4); Closed Gentian (5); Fringed Gentian (6).

scented. It flowers from May to October. A species living in the pine forests of the western United States has white petals veined with rose.

Two unusual woodland flowers of moist thickets and stream margins are the fringed and the closed gentians. FRINGED GENTIAN has a dark-blue flower, borne singly or in small clusters at the tip of the angular erect stem. Ovate leaves occur opposite each other along the stem, which grows to a height of several feet. Fringed gentian flowers have a regular perianth, with the parts fused to form a cylindrical green ridged calyx and a tubular corolla. The corolla, an inch or two in length, has a four-lobed and fringed margin. This and the following species are unusual members of the woodland community, in flower as late as August and September. Fringed gentian is found throughout eastern United States.

CLOSED GENTIAN, or bottle gentian, is also an inhabitant of the moist woods of the northeastern United States and Canada. Stout unbranched stems, usually less than two feet in height, bear opposite lanceolate leaves and a dense terminal cluster of flowers surrounded by green leafy bracts. Each flower is about one inch in length, with a tubular corolla; the corolla has a four- or five-lobed margin which remains closed, giving the flower a bottle-like or clublike appearance. Several other species of gentian, with creamy white as well as lilac-tinted flowers, have established themselves in the salt-marsh habitats of northern North America. Additional species, white or blue in color, occur in the western United States.

SPIDERWORT is a wild flower that makes its home along shaded roadsides as well as in woods and open thickets of the eastern United States. It grows to a height of several feet, with lanceolate grasslike leaves which clasp the stem. Spiderwort is a Monocot, as is indicated by the perianth of three sepals and three petals. The dark blue or purple regular flowers, an inch or two in diameter and growing in small terminal umbels, are very short-lived, opening in the morning and withering by noon. Spiderwort is in flower from April through July.

SCORPIONWEED is found in the open woods of the central United States, where it flowers during April and May. It is a stiff, hairy-stemmed plant with pinnately lobed leaves. Small regular blue flowers, each less than one-half inch in diameter, grow in curved racemes. The petals of the bell-shaped flower are fused at the base to form a tubular corolla with five fringed lobes. A number of related species in the southern and western states have white flowers, others blue; some of these are members of the xerophytic communities of the southwestern states.

A common BLUE VIOLET of wooded meadows throughout the eastern United States is a stemless species with triangular or cordate leaves which often hide the deep blue flower on its elongated flower stalk. The irregular flower, like that of all violets, is spurred. Many species of blue violets grow in North American woodlands, the majority flowering in April and May.

WILD BLUE PHLOX prefers to grow in the open sandy woods of the central United States. It is a matted plant with spreading stems, some of which curve upward and bear dense terminal clusters of blue flowers. The opposite leaves are oblong in shape; leaflike bracts surround the base of the flower cluster. Each flower has a regular

123

perianth with a five-lobed calyx and a tubular corolla expanding saucerlike with a five-lobed margin. Wild blue phlox can be found in flower from April to June.

Three of the typical blue woodland flowers have irregular perianths: dwarf larkspur, blue-eyed Mary, and Chinese houses. DWARF LARKSPUR is a blue-flowered species growing on wooded slopes in eastern United States, rarely found as far north as New England. It has palmately lobed leaves, and grows to a height of three or four feet. Large flowers, each about an inch in length, grow in terminal racemes. As in the scarlet larkspur we have already met, the irregular perianth consists of five petal-like sepals and four petals; one of the sepals and two petals are spurred. Some of the western larkspurs are able to live in arid habitats and thus can be found in the xerophytic communities of the southwestern United States.

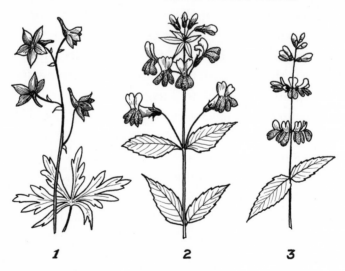

Blue or Blue-and-white Woodland Flowers: Dwarf Larkspur (1); Blue-eyed Mary (2); Chinese Houses (3).

124

BLUE-EYED MARY, a wild flower of the southern and central woodlands, is a low-growing plant, rarely more than twenty inches tall. The leaves are opposite and elliptical, the flowers develop in open terminal racemes. The irregular corolla, a half inch in length, is two-lipped and is unusual in being bicolored. The two-lobed upper lip is white, the lower lip is three-lobed and blue. In April, the flowers of blue-eyed Mary appear and continue to bloom until June.

In woodlands west of the Rocky Mountains one finds the colorful CHINESE HOUSES, a relative of blue-eyed Mary. This is a plant of the same size, growing a foot or two in height, with similar bicolored flowers; the lanceolate leaves are opposite or whorled. Chinese houses develops its flowers in whorls at the tips of the stems; the two-lobed upper lip of each flower is white, the three-lobed lower lip is violet or rose-purple.

The preceding blue flowers are inhabitants of rich, moist, and shaded woods. Other species with blue flowers establish themselves in drier, more rocky habitats with greater exposure to bright sunlight. In this group we find hepatica, wild hyacinth, wild comfrey, harebell, tall bellflower, lyre-leaved sage, and blazing star. Of these, lyre-leaved sage is the only species with an irregular perianth, and blazing star is the only species with its flowers in a head.

ROUND-LEAVED HEPATICA, also known as liverleaf, is one of the most familiar early spring wild flowers of the eastern United States. Often it can be found in bloom as early as March, while the deciduous trees above it are still leafless; it continues in flower until June. Rounded, three-lobed leaves are semievergreen, persisting through

125

the winter; they rise only a few inches above the ground. In spring, slender hairy stems raise clusters of solitary flowers above the old foliage; fresh leaves appear after the flowering period. The regular flowers, about one-half inch in diameter, range in color from blue to purple, lavender, and white. Hepatica is a species in the Buttercup family, and like many of its relatives, has colored sepals but no petals; the sepals vary in number from five to seven. Hepatica is a hardy member of the woods community, extending its range north to Alaska. SHARP-LOBED HEPATICA, with more pointed leaf lobes, is common in the woods of the central and southern United States.

WILD HYACINTH, also called squill, is an onionlike plant of open woods in the eastern and southern United States. It grows from a bulb, and like many other Monocots has grasslike leaves with parallel venation. A leafless flower stalk, twelve to eighteen inches in height, bears a terminal cluster of star-shaped flowers, each about one inch in diameter. The six perianth segments are alike, both sepals and petals being a lilac-blue. Wild hyacinth flowers from May to June.

WILD COMFREY, or hound's tongue, lives in open deciduous woods of the eastern and southern United States. It is a bristly-hairy plant, growing to a height of several feet, with alternate lanceolate leaves clasping the stem. Small blue flowers, about one-quarter inch in diameter, are clustered in a loose terminal raceme. Each flower has a cuplike and five-lobed green calyx, and a regular funnel-shaped corolla formed by the fusion of the petals. The margin of the corolla is five-lobed also. Wild comfrey blooms from April to June. The fruits, maturing in summer, are bristly and thus cling to the fur of animals as a means of dispersal.

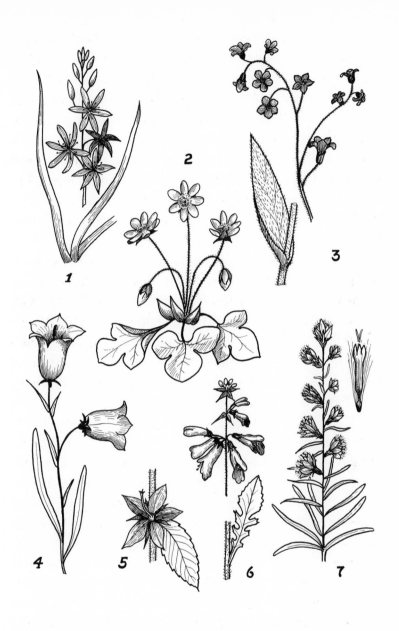

Blue or Purple Woodland Flowers: Wild Hyacinth (1); *Hepatica* (2); *Wild Comfrey* (3); *Harebell* (4); *Bellflower* (5); *Lyre-leaved Sage* (6); *Blazing Star* (7).

HAREBELL, or bluebell, thrives in open sandy or rocky habitats in the cooler northeastern portion of the United States. It is a slender-stemmed plant with rounded basal leaves and linear, grasslike leaves along the stems. Deep blue, regular flowers, about one-half inch in diameter, grow singly or in small terminal clusters. Each flower is bell-shaped, with a tubular corolla resulting from complete fusion of the petals; the margin has five shallow lobes. The flowers appear in July and continue in bloom until September. Harebell is an extremely adaptable wild flower, with habitats that vary from exposed arctic-alpine situations to protected mesophytic meadows; in sheltered locations it grows taller and has larger leaves and flowers. In rocky woodlands of the southern states, one finds SOUTHERN HAREBELL with paler blue flowers. TALL BELL-FLOWER, another relative, grows in the moister woodlands of the eastern United States, reaching a stature of six feet and bearing in the upper leaf axils large showy blue flowers,.an inch in diameter.

LYRE-LEAVED SAGE, a member of the Mint family, grows in the open sandy woods of the eastern United States. It has the square stem and aromatic foliage characteristic of the family. Lyre-leaved sage grows a foot or two in height, with oval, pinnately lobed leaves growing opposite each other. Lavender blue flowers are borne in elongated compact clusters, in whorls of three to ten flowers near the tip of the stem. Each flower, about an inch in length, has a tubular corolla which is irregular and two-lipped. The upper lip is straight; the spreading lower lip is three-lobed with a large middle lobe. Lyre-leaved sage can be found in flower from April through June.

128

SOUTHERN BLAZING STAR is a showy wild flower of southern pinelands and dry woods. Unbranched stems, bearing simple narrow leaves growing alternately on the stem, reach a height of three or four feet. The stems terminate in a spire of purplish flower heads. Each head consists of tubular disk flowers only, seated in a cluster of green bracts that often have petal-like tips as long as the corolla. Southern blazing star blooms in summer, from June to September. This is only one of many species of blazing star found in the central portion of the United States.

Wild-Flower Saprophytes and Parasites

Green is the characteristic color of the plant kingdom, because of the presence of chlorophyll by which such plants manufacture their own food through the process of photosynthesis. Many plants, however, lack this unique green pigment and as a result are colorless, or, if colored, are not green. The largest group of nongreen plants are the fungi: mushrooms, molds, and mildews. These plants never produce flowers. A few nongreen plants do have flowers, but because of their white or yellowish-brown color and absence of leaves are often mistaken for fungi. The most familiar of these nongreen flowering plants is Indian pipe.

Plants without chlorophyll, being unable to carry on photosynthesis, cannot manufacture their own food. Instead they must absorb it from outside their bodies. If a plant secures its food from the organic remains of dead plants or animals, it is a *saprophyte;* if the plant obtains its food from the body of a living organism, it is a *parasite*. Many saprophytes get their food from the organic litter that forms humus in the soil. Many plant parasites absorb their food from the roots or stems of living green plants.

Among the independent green wild flowers of the woodland community live a few saprophytes and parasites. Their leaves have either become reduced to white scales or sheaths, or have entirely disappeared. The stems are also white, yellow, brown, or even bright red. The roots are especially adapted for absorption of organic food. These unusual wild flowers occur in three families of flowering plants: the Heath, Broom-rape, and Orchid families. In the Heath family we find Indian pipe, pinesap, pinedrops, sweet pinesap, and snow plant. In the Broom-rape family are cancer-root, squawroot, and beechdrops. Among the orchids without chlorophyll are phantom orchid, coralroot, and brunetta.

INDIAN PIPE is a ghostly white or pinkish saprophyte of damp shaded woods, found throughout North America wherever the soil is rich in humus. It also has the appropriate name of corpse plant. Clusters of erect stems, eight to ten inches in height, rise from a ball of matted roots. Each stem bears colorless scales instead of leaves, and terminates in a single nodding white flower with a regular corolla of four or five separate petals. Each flower is one-half inch to one inch in length. The flowers appear from June to September, being especially common after long wet and rainy spells of weather. After fertilization, Indian pipe changes the posture of the flower so that the perianth becomes erect. At this time the entire plant turns brown or black.

130

Indian pipe is one of the saprophyte members of the woodland community, often mistaken for a fungus because of its lack of chlorophyll.

PINESAP, also a saprophyte, is lemon-yellow in color and grows in the more open, sandy woods of the eastern United States. Erect hairy stems, with scales in place of leaves, grow to a height of eight to ten inches. Fragrant flowers, each about one inch in length, are borne in a drooping terminal raceme. Each flower has a regular perianth with four or five sepals, and five petals. The flowers appear in July and August.

PINEDROPS is a stouter, purplish plant living as a parasite on the roots of pines in the northern United States and Canada. It also is found on the Pacific coast where it grows in the humus-rich soil of conifer forests at altitudes of 5,000 to 8,500 feet. Erect stems, covered with scales, grow to a height of several feet and bear nodding flowers in large terminal racemes. Each flower is urn-shaped and white or reddish in color; the regular corolla has a tubular base and a five-toothed margin. It flowers from June to August.

SWEET PINESAP, a smaller plant rarely more than six inches in height, inhabits moist acid woods of the southeastern United States, where it can be found in flower from March to May. Fragrant white or pink flowers are clustered in a raceme; each flower has a regular tubular corolla with a five-lobed margin.

SNOW PLANT is an exception, in its scarlet coloring, to the usual more drab saprophytes. This conspicuous fleshy plant grows in the rich soil beneath the redwoods and other conifers of the California forests, at altitudes between 5,000 and 8,000 feet. The stout stem, completely covered with scales, grows to a height of eight to ten inches and terminates in a broad spike of red flowers mingled with

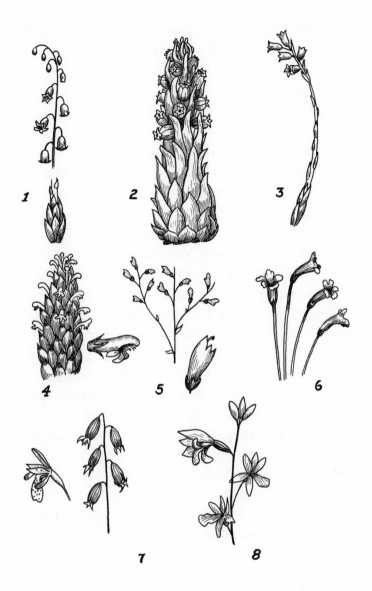

Wild flower Saprophytes and Parasites: Pinedrops (1); Snow Plant (2); Pinesap (3); Squawroot (4); Beechdrops (5); Cancer-root (6); Coralroot (7); Brunetta (8).

long scales. Each flower, about one-half inch in length, has a regular perianth of five sepals and a bell-shaped five-lobed corolla. Snow plant is appropriately named because it often pushes its way through the partly frozen soil of early spring while the snow patches still linger beneath the trees.

The Broom-rape family is a large one, with over two hundred species of root parasites. CANCER-ROOT, also known as broom-rape, grows in rich woods throughout North America, being in flower during May and June. The matted roots absorb nourishment from the roots of deciduous green plants of the forest community. Cancer-root is a slender unbranched plant, its stem covered with scales, growing only a few inches tall. Each brownish stem terminates in a solitary arching flower with a pinkish-brown, bell-shaped, five-lobed corolla less than an inch in length. The flowers are irregular and two-lipped; the upper lip is two-lobed, the lower lip three-lobed.

SQUAWROOT, a stout yellowish-brown parasite, grows only four to eight inches tall, the unbranched stem being covered with scales. Scales also form bracts among the flowers of the terminal spike. Young plants resemble erect pine cones, or form rounded knobs on the exposed roots of trees. Each flower has an irregular perianth with a yellow two-lipped corolla; the upper lip is concave, and the three-lobed lower lip is spreading. Squawroot can be found in flower from April to July.

BEECHDROPS differs from its relatives in the Broom-rape family by having branching stems and growing to a height of twelve inches; the stems bear scattered clusters of yellowish-brown or purplish flowers in racemes or spikes. Each flower, less than one-half inch in length, is irregular and has a curved, tubular corolla. The corolla is two-lipped, although, to the casual observer, the upper lip being slightly notched and the lower lip shallowly lobed, it appears to be a four-toothed flower. Beechdrops, as the name indicates, is parasitic on the roots of beech trees and thus occurs chiefly in the eastern United States.

The Orchid family includes three unusual saprophytes that form part of the forest community. PHANTOM ORCHID is a stout white plant found in the Pacific coast pine forests, with a creeping rootstock and fleshy roots that obtain nourishment from the humus-rich forest floor. Stems, clothed in colorless sheathing bracts, grow to a height of sixteen inches and terminate in a spike of yellowish flowers. Each flower, about one-half inch in length, has the typical irregular orchid perianth; the lower lip is ornamented with conspicuous wavy crests.

CORALROOT is a brownish or purplish orchid that lives either as a saprophyte or a parasite in rich forest humus throughout the United States. The name refers to the toothed and coral-like underground stems. Erect unbranched flower stalks, a foot or two in height, terminate in a raceme of irregular purplish flowers, each less than one-half inch in length. The corolla has a deeply three-lobed and whitish lip which is spotted with purple. Coralroot is one of a half dozen species with similar habits and general appearance; they flower in the spring.

BRUNETTA is a saprophyte living in the woods of the southeastern United States; its nearest relatives live in Mexico. This wild flower has brown stems, growing to a height of several feet and bearing scalelike leaves. Purplish brown flowers grow in a large terminal raceme that reaches a length of twelve inches. Each flower has an irregular corolla with a crested lower lip; the flowers appear during the summer.

This ends our excursion into the woods, forests, and roadside thickets of the United States. Even though the number of wild flowers described may seem a large assemblage, they are only a small portion of the entire woodland community. The flowers selected are among the most common and those most likely to be encountered in accessible locations. It will be easier to identify these flowers if we think of them in groups on the basis of the kind of habitat in which they grow; their geographic range; and the significant features of their foliage, habits, or flowers. A little practice in using the clues given in the following tables will lead to recognition of the wild flowers we have met, by name. This in turn will make any young naturalist feel at home among the plants of the woods and forests.

HOW TO IDENTIFY SOME WHITE WOODLAND FLOWERS

Clue No. 1. What is the general habit of the plant?

If prostrate, trailing, or vinelike, go to Clue No. 2.
If erect, go to Clue No. 5.

Clue No. 2. Are the petals separate or fused into a tubular corolla?

If separate, flowers in an open raceme .... SPRING BEAUTY.
If the corolla is tubular or urn-shaped, go to Clue No. 3.

Clue No. 3. How are the flowers arranged on the plant?

If solitary or in pairs, go to Clue No. 4.
If in clusters .... MAYFLOWER.

Clue No. 4. How are the leaves arranged on the stems?

If alternate, flowers nodding .... CHECKERBERRY.
If opposite, flowers erect .... PARTRIDGEBERRY.

Clue No. 5. How large are the flowers?

If less than ½ inch in diameter, go to Clue No. 6.
If more than ½ inch in diameter, go to Clue No. 9.

Clue No. 6. What is the type of leaf venation?

If netted veined (Dicot type), go to Clue No. 7.
If parallel veined (Monocot type), go to Clue No. 8.

Clue No. 7. Are accessory floral structures present?

If white petal-like bracts are present beneath the flowers .....
.... BUNCHBERRY.
If petal-like bracts are absent .... SAXIFRAGE.

Clue No. 8. How large is the plant?

If six inches or less in height, flowers in raceme ....
.... CANADA MAYFLOWER.
If a foot or more in height, flowers in panicle ....
.... FALSE SOLOMON'S SEAL.

Clue No. 9. How are the flowers arranged on the plant?

If solitary or in small clusters, go to Clue No. 10.
If in racemes or umbels, go to Clue No. 15.

Clue No. 10. How many perianth segments are there?

If six, go to Clue No. 11.
If four, five, or an indefinite number, go to Clue No. 12.

Clue No. 11. Is the perianth differentiated into sepals and petals?

If *three green sepals, three colored petals* .... TRILLIUM.

If *three white sepals, three white petals, colored alike* ....

.... ATAMASCO LILY.

Clue No. 12. Are the leaves simple or compound?

If *simple, lobed* .... BLOODROOT.

If *compound, go to Clue No. 13.*

Clue No. 13. Are the flowers solitary or clustered?

If *clustered* .... RUE ANEMONE.

If *solitary, go to Clue No. 14.*

Clue No. 14. What relation do the leaves bear to the flowers?

If *umbrellalike, above the nodding flower* ...... MAY APPLE.

If *not umbrellalike, beneath the erect flower* . WOOD ANEMONE.

Clue No. 15. What is the type of leaf venation?

If *parallel, leaves grasslike (Monocot type)* .... CAMASS.

If *netted (Dicot type), go to Clue No. 16.*

Clue No. 16. What is the shape of the leaves?

If *lobed (western U.S. only)* .... WOODLAND STAR.

If *not lobed (eastern species), go to Clue No. 17.*

Clue No. 17. What is the type of inflorescence?

If *a drooping umbel* .... PIPSISSEWA.

If *an erect raceme, go to Clue No. 18.*

Clue No. 18. Are the leaves evergreen or deciduous?

If *evergreen* .... ROUND-LEAVED WINTERGREEN.

If *deciduous* .... SHINLEAF.

HOW TO IDENTIFY SOME YELLOW WOODLAND
FLOWERS

Clue No. 1. How are the flowers arranged on the plant?

If *solitary or in small clusters, go to Clue No. 2.*

If *in a definite inflorescence, go to Clue No. 6.*

Clue No. 2. What type of symmetry does the perianth have?

If *regular, go to Clue No. 3.*

If *irregular, go to Clue No. 5.*

138

Clue No. 3 Is a stem present or absent?

Stemless plants, flowers rising from the ground ....
.... DOGTOOTH VIOLET.
Plants with erect stems, go to Clue No. 4.

Clue No. 4. How are the leaves attached to the stem?

If base of leaf encircles stem .... BELLWORT.
If leaves are sessile, not encircling stem .... WILD OATS.

Clue No. 5. What is the shape of the corolla?

If one petal forms an inflated sac .... YELLOW LADY'S SLIPPER.
If one petal forms a spur .... YELLOW VIOLET.

Clue No. 6. What is the type of inflorescence?

If a daisylike head (composite) .... CUP PLANT.
If a compact spike; pinnately lobed leaves .... WOOD BETONY.
If a raceme or umbel, go to Clue No. 7.

Clue No. 7. What type of symmetry does the perianth have?

If regular, go to Clue No. 8.
If irregular, go to Clue No. 9.

Clue No. 8. What are the color and size of the perianth?

If orange-yellow, over two inches long (western U.S.) ......
.... HUMBOLDT LILY.
If greenish-yellow, less than an inch (eastern U.S.) . DOGBERRY.

Clue No. 9. What is the shape of the corolla?

If petals form divergent large spurs .. DUTCHMAN'S BREECHES.
If petals form short rounded spurs .... SQUIRREL CORN.

HOW TO IDENTIFY SOME RED OR
PINK WOODLAND FLOWERS

Clue No. 1. What is the general habit of the plant?

If it is prostrate and trailing .... MOSS PINK.
If erect, go to Clue No. 2.

Clue No. 2. What type of symmetry does the perianth have?

If it is regular, go to Clue No. 3.
If it is irregular, go to Clue No. 10.

Clue No. 3. How many perianth segments are there?

If in fours or fives, go to Clue No. 4.
If in threes or sixes, go to Clue No. 5.

Clue No. 4. Is the corolla tubular or made up of separate petals?

If tubular, with lobed margin .... CENTAURY.
If of separate segments, colored alike .... COLUMBINE.

Clue No. 5. Are the petals different from the sepals?

If perianth consists of three green sepals, three colored petals .
.... TRILLIUM.
If perianth consists of six similar segments, go to Clue No. 6.

Clue No. 6. How large are the flowers?

If less than an inch in length .... TWISTED STALK.
If more than an inch in length, go to Clue No. 7.

Clue No. 7. What is the position of the flower?

If erect, go to Clue No. 8.
If nodding, go to Clue No. 9.

Clue No. 8. What is the shape of the petals?

If pointed, with narrowed basal portions .... WOOD LILY.
If rounded, with tapering basal portions (southeastern U.S.)
.... LEOPARD LILY.

Clue No. 9. What is the shape of the leaves?

If lanceolate (throughout eastern U.S.) ... TURK'S-CAP LILY.
If nearly ovate, blunt-tipped (southern U.S. only) ....
.... CAROLINA LILY.

Clue No. 10. What is the type of inflorescence?

If a spirelike raceme, flowers scarlet ..... SCARLET LARKSPUR.
If solitary, flowers pink .... MOCCASIN FLOWER.

HOW TO IDENTIFY SOME BLUE OR PURPLE
WOODLAND FLOWERS

Clue No. 1. What type of symmetry does the perianth have?
If regular, go to Clue No. 2.
If irregular, go to Clue No. 12.

140

Clue No. 2. How many perianth segments are there?

If segments are in fours or fives (Dicot type), go to Clue No. 4.

If segments are in threes or sixes (Monocot type), go to Clue No. 3.

Clue No. 3. Is the corolla differentiated into petals and sepals?

If there are three green sepals, three colored petals SPIDERWORT.

If there are six segments, colored alike .... WATER HYACINTH.

Clue No. 4. Is the corolla tubular or made up of separate petals?

If the petals are separate, go to Clue No. 5.

If the petals are fused to form a tube, go to Clue No. 7.

Clue No. 5. What is the general habit of the plant?

If low-growing, stemless .... HEPATICA.

If erect, more than six inches above the ground, go to Clue No. 6.

Clue No. 6. How large are the flowers?

If a half inch in diameter, leaflets lobed ...... HERB ROBERT.

If an inch in diameter, leaflets toothed ..... WILD GERANIUM.

Clue No. 7. How are the flowers arranged on the plant?

If many small flowers in heads, forming terminal spire ......
.... BLAZING STAR.

If flowers are not in heads, go to Clue No. 8.

Clue No. 8. What is the nature of the corolla lobes?

If the margin is fringed, go to Clue No. 9.

If the margin is entire, go to Clue No. 10.

Clue No. 9. What types of leaves are present?

If entire and opposite .... FRINGED GENTIAN.

If pinnately lobed and alternate .... SCORPIONWEED.

Clue No. 10. How are the leaves arranged on the plant?

If opposite each other .... CLOSED GENTIAN.

If alternate with each other, go to Clue No. 11.

Clue No. 11. What is the nature of the stems?

If bristly .... WILD COMFREY.

If smooth, linear leaves, plants 1–2 feet tall ...... HAREBELL.

If smooth, lanceolate leaves, plants 4–6 feet tall ....
.... TALL BELLFLOWER.

Clue No. 12. How are the flowers arranged on the plant?

>If *solitary* .... BLUE VIOLET.
>If *in an inflorescence, go to Clue No. 13.*

Clue No. 13. How is the corolla colored?

>If *it is bicolored, go to Clue No. 14.*
>If *it is all of one color, go to Clue No. 15.*

Clue No. 14. What is the color of the lower lip?

>If *light blue (eastern U.S.)* .... BLUE-EYED MARY.
>If *rose-purple (western U.S.)* .... CHINESE HOUSES.

Clue No. 15. What is the nature of the stems?

>If *round, corolla spurred* .... LARKSPUR.
>If *square, corolla two-lipped* .... SAGE.

HOW TO IDENTIFY WILD FLOWERS LACKING IN CHLOROPHYLL

Clue No. 1. How are the flowers arranged on the plant?

>If *solitary, go to Clue No. 2.*
>If *clustered or in a definite inflorescence, go to Clue No. 3.*

Clue No. 2. What is the color of the plant?

>If *white or pinkish* .... INDIAN PIPE.
>If *creamy brown* .... CANCER-ROOT.

Clue No. 3. What is the color of the plant?

>If *bright red (western U.S. only)* .... SNOW PLANT.
>If *yellow, brown, or purple, go to Clue. No. 4.*

Clue No. 4. What type of symmetry does the perianth have?

>If *regular, go to Clue No. 5.*
>If *irregular, go to Clue No. 7.*

Clue No. 5 Are the petals separate or united?

>If *separate* .... PINESAP.
>If *fused to form a tubular flower, go to Clue No. 6.*

Clue No. 6. How large is the plant?

>If *it is six inches or less in height* .... PINEDROPS.
>If *twelve inches or more in height* .... SWEET PINESAP.

142

Clue No. 7. What type of stem does the plant have?

If it is branched, with scattered flower clusters .. BEECHDROPS.

If it is unbranched, stout and conelike .... SQUAWROOT.

If it is unbranched and slender, go to Clue No. 8.

Clue No. 8. Is the lower lip of the corolla smooth or crested?

If smooth .... CORALROOT.

If crested, go to Clue No. 9.

Clue No. 9. Where does the plant grow?

If in the southeastern United States .... BRUNETTA.

If in the western United States .... PHANTOM ORCHID.

The sunflower is a giant among the many composites in our field wild-flower community; the inflorescence (*head*) consists of a rim of yellow ray flowers and a central disk of many dark-brown tubular flowers.

CHAPTER SIX

FLOWERS OF FIELDS AND ROADSIDES

We began our visits to the homes of wild flowers with those where the environment provided a great deal of water. There we saw communities of hydrophytes adapted for living in ponds and streams, in swamps and bogs. We continued our exploration and found, in the shaded and protected habitats of woods and forests, communities where mesophytic wild flowers have their homes. Leaving the sheltered environment of the forests, we now complete our tour of the different types of plant communities by becoming familiar with the fields and roadsides, grasslands and waste places where xerophytes make their home.

In many such habitats the intense sunlight and exposure to the elements bring about excessive transpiration. Plants living in such environments must be adapted for securing the little water available as well as conserving what water they have absorbed. Added to the critical transpiration factor is another unfavorable condition, that of poor sandy or rocky soil. Wild flowers in this environment must have deep or penetrating root systems and foliage of thick or hairy leaves, small leaves, or leaves in flat basal rosettes. Many of these plants have spiny or prickly foliage to discourage herbivorous animals that can find little food in such habitats. A great number of immigrant species, because of their hardiness and ability to survive adverse living conditions, thrive in these xerophytic surroundings.

The treeless plains of the central United States constitute a vast grassland domain in which such plant communities prosper. Old fields and pastures, roadside banks and burned-over areas found throughout the eastern United States also provide suitable environments for plants with xerophytic tendencies. When the factor of high temperatures is added, as in the desert regions of the southwestern United States, the environment becomes the home of the most extreme xerophytes, those that enable them to live under the seemingly impossible conditions of minimum rainfall, intense sunlight and heat, and poor soil.

The most spectacular mass display of wild flowers occurs in fields and along roadsides. In New England, during the height of summer, it is made up of snowy white fields of daisies; in autumn, of the blue-and-gold of asters and goldenrods. In the prairie states the flower display covers many acres of golden yellow sunflowers, or the miles of rolling hills dyed blue by fields of bluebonnets. The grassy slopes of the California foothills are converted each spring into a riot of color with the blooming of purple owl's-clover, blue lupine, and golden poppies. Most spectacular sight of all is the transformation of desert land, after spring rains, into the colorful wild-flower gardens of the Colorado and Mojave deserts in Southern California. Suddenly the drab earth becomes lavender and white and gold with millions of verbena, desert primroses, and gold-fields. Adding a showy display of their own are the cacti, with their surprisingly fragile blossoms in yellow, pink, lavender, and red tints.

Green and Greenish-White Flowers

Two common wild flowers of roadsides and clearings have green or greenish-white flowers: ragweed and silverrod. Both are members of the Composite family and thus have flowers in heads. RAGWEED is a rank-growing plant with large pinnately lobed leaves whose lobes are toothed or indented. Inconspicuous green flowers, barely visible without a hand lens, are borne in two types of heads. One type is made up of staminate flowers, the other of pistillate ones. Staminate heads are clustered in slender nodding spikes at the tips of the branches. Each minute staminate flower has a tubular, lobed corolla. Pistillate heads are grouped in globular and nutlike involucres seated in the leaf axils beneath the staminate spikes. Each pistillate flower has a reduced perianth, often no corolla at all. The ragweed of the eastern United States grows to a height of five feet, and flowers from July to October. A western GREAT RAG-WEED grows fifteen feet tall. Ragweeds are among the chief offenders in causing hay fever.

SILVERROD, a greenish or silvery white flower of the goldenrod group, is a slender plant with an erect un-

147

branching stem, one to two feet tall, bearing alternate lanceolate leaves. Each head, less than one-eighth inch in size, has small whitish ray flowers. The heads are arranged in elongated and slender spires. Silverrod is common throughout the eastern United States; it flowers from July to October. Its favorite habitats include roadside fields and clearings in woods.

White Flowers

For ease of identification, we can separate the white flowers of the fields-and-roadsides community into three groups, based on their geographic occurrence. One group includes wild flowers that have spread throughout the United States. This consists of chickweed, thorn apple, Queen Anne's lace, yarrow, and pearly everlasting. A second group is found only in the eastern United States. This includes such familiar roadside wild flowers as bladder campion, sandwort, wild strawberry, white daisy, and white aster. A third group is restricted to the western states: horsemint, sand verbena, prickly and Matilija poppies, cream-cups, and soap plant. This last group also includes the desert xerophytes with white flowers, such as desert primrose, desert lily, and desert star.

COMMON CHICKWEED thrives in dry fields and grassy places in all our states. It is a weak-stemmed trailing plant with slender stems and opposite ovate leaves. Small flowers, less than one-quarter inch in diameter, grow in spreading clusters. Each flower has a regular perianth of five sepals and five separate petals; the petals are so deeply

148

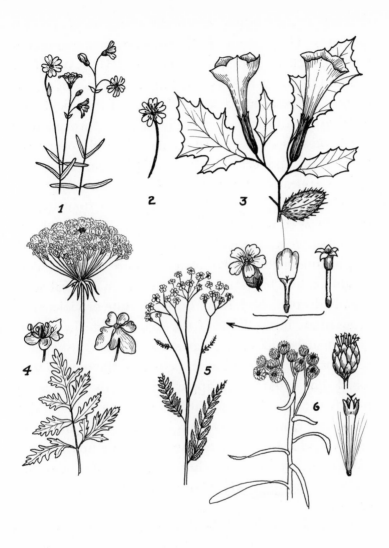

White Field Flowers: Field Chickweed (1); *Common Chick-weed* (2); *Thorn Apple* (3); *Queen Anne's Lace* (4); *Yarrow* (5); *Pearly Everlasting* (6).

notched at the tip that the corolla seems to consist of ten segments. This species of chickweed flowers continuously from March to November. FIELD CHICKWEED has similar but larger flowers, reaching a diameter of one-half inch; each petal has a squared notched tip. Field chickweed grows in rocky or gravelly habitats throughout the northern states. Its matted stems are rarely over twelve inches tall, and bear small opposite linear leaves. The flowers appear in April and bloom through July.

THORN APPLE, or Jimsonweed, is a stout-stemmed roadside weed which has immigrated to the United States from Asia; it is a member of the Nightshade family, which also includes petunia and tobacco. Thorn apple grows to a height of five feet, and has large alternate oval leaves, usually deeply lobed. Erect flowers, white or violet-tinted, grow singly in the forks of the stems. Each flower, three or four inches in length, has a regular funnel-shaped corolla formed by the fusion of the petals; the margin is five-lobed. The name "thorn apple" refers to the fruit, an oval prickly capsule about two inches in length. Leaves, stems, roots, and fruits are poisonous because of the presence of an alkaloid known as hyoscyamine. Cattle and horses die from eating the foliage; children have been poisoned by eating the unripe fruits. Thorn apple flowers from July to October.

QUEEN ANNE'S LACE, or wild carrot, grows commonly in open fields and roadsides. It is a bristly-stemmed plant growing to a height of three feet, with fernlike and pinnately compound leaves. Small, slightly irregular flowers, less than one-quarter inch in diameter, grow in terminal umbels, which in turn are grouped into larger flat-

150

topped umbels. Each flower has five small sepals and five slightly unequal petals. A unique feature is the one dark purple flower in the middle of each umbel. Queen Anne's lace is in flower from May to October.

YARROW, or milfoil, is another wayside flower with ferny, pinnately compound leaves; the foliage of this species is aromatic, and borne on stiffly erect stems that grow to a height of several feet. Yarrow is a member of the Composite family, with flowers in small heads grouped in a spreading and flat-topped cluster several inches broad. Each head consists of minute yellowish disk flowers surrounded by four or five white ray flowers each less than an eighth-inch in length. Some varieties of yarrow have pink or purplish ray flowers. Yarrow is a long-blooming plant, with flowers from June through September.

PEARLY EVERLASTING, found in sunny fields, is distinctive because of the woolly, silvery foliage and the pearly white involucre that surrounds the small flower heads. Pearly everlasting, also a composite, grows to a height of three feet and bears alternate lanceolate leaves. The small flower heads, borne in terminal clusters, have involucres that are far more conspicuous than the small five-toothed pistillate flowers or the staminate flowers with threadlike corollas. Pearly everlasting can be found in flower during late summer, in July and August. The dry chaffy involucres last indefinitely; hence the plants are often used for indoor ornamental purposes. Florists, to give them brighter colors, often dye these dried wild flowers red or blue.

BLADDER CAMPION is a member of the Pink family found along roadsides and in fields of the eastern United

151

States. It is one of over a dozen related wild flowers, some of which are known as catchly. Bladder campion grows several feet tall, with opposite lanceolate or ovate leaves and nodding flowers in spreading terminal clusters. Each regular flower, slightly less than one inch in diameter, has a bladderlike inflated calyx formed by the fusion of the sepals. The five separate petals are each deeply two-lobed, resulting in a corolla with apparently ten slender petals. Bladder campion flowers from April to August.

SANDWORT, also a member of the Pink family, occurs in dry gravelly and sandy habitats of the eastern United States. Wiry stems, growing a foot in height, bear rigid and linear clustered leaves. The flowers grow in a loose terminal cluster. Sandwort differs from bladder campion in having separate sepals forming a less conspicuous calyx. The regular corolla consists of five entire petals,

White Field Flowers: Bladder Campion (1); *Sandwort* (2);
Wild Strawberry (3); *White Daisy* (4); *White Aster* (5).

much longer than the sepals. Sandwort is in flower from May through July.

WILD STRAWBERRY, a familiar low-growing plant of open sunny fields, is far better known for its juicy fruit than for its flowers. Wild strawberry grows in sandy soils throughout the eastern United States. The prostrate stems root at the nodes, and bear compound leaves with three serrate leaflets. Small clusters of flowers grow amid the foliage, each flower being about one-half inch in diameter with a regular perianth of five green sepals and five separate rounded petals. Wild strawberry, a member of the Rose family, flowers from April through June. In early summer the red berries develop, each an enlarged and fleshy receptacle beneath the perianth; the actual fruits are nutlike achenes, and are the small specks seen on the surface of the berry.

Several of the white field flowers of the eastern United States are composites, with the typical head made up of ray and disk flowers. WHITE DAISY, a European immigrant related to the chrysanthemum, has made itself so thoroughly at home in the field community that it seems a part of our native flora. A basal group of rounded or oblong leaves give rise to an erect stem, two or three feet tall, which bears toothed or pinnately lobed lanceolate leaves. The flower heads, one inch or more in diameter, usually grow singly at the tips of the stems. Each head is seated in a saucerlike involucre of green bracts. The margin of the head is made up of ten to twenty white ray flowers, each with a narrow strap-shaped corolla; the center of the head is a compact mass of yellow tubular disk flowers. White daisies are the heralds of midsummer, blooming in profusion during July and early August.

153

WHITE ASTER is a plant of fields and open woods of the eastern United States and Canada. It has a zigzag stem, a foot or two in height, bearing cordate leaves and terminating in a flat-topped cluster of many flower heads, each about three-quarters of an inch in diameter. Each head consists of from six to nine white ray flowers and a compact central disk of yellow or purplish tubular flowers. This species of aster is in flower from July to October. Like its relatives with purple and blue flowers, white aster is one of the autumn wild flowers of New England. CALICO ASTER, or starved aster, is a pale-blue or white aster growing to a height of four feet, with ovate basal leaves and lanceolate stem leaves. Small flower heads, each less than one-half an inch in diameter, grow in one-sided racemes. Each head has from nine to fifteen ray flowers and a disk of purplish tubular flowers.

Grassy hillsides and fields in the western United States include some wildflower members that do not occur in the eastern states. HORSEMINT, a member of the Mint family, has erect stems several feet in height with opposite lanceolate leaves, and irregular flowers, often with a yellowish tinge, in dense axillary clusters mingled with purplish leaflike bracts. Each flower, about one-half inch in length, has a five-lobed and ribbed tubular calyx, and a two-lipped corolla with a dilated throat. The upper lip is narrow and arched, the lower lip is spreading and three-lobed. Horsemint is in flower during June and July.

SAND VERBENA, or white abronia, belongs to the Four-o'clock family, which is characterized by flowers that lack petals but have a colored calyx. Sand verbena is a

Prickly poppy is a prickly leaved, bushy plant which displays its large white flowers on dry slopes of the central United States.

trailing plant of dry sandy habitats, with stems enlarged at the nodes and bearing opposite ovate or elliptical leaves. Small irregular flowers grow in axillary or terminal clusters, mingled with leaflike bracts; each flower has a tubular, four- or five-lobed white calyx. The flowers appear in late summer, opening only at night. This species of verbena is common in the western prairie states.

Two of the showiest of the white field flowers found west of the Mississippi River are members of the Poppy family. **PRICKLY POPPY** is a thistlelike plant with spiny foliage, growing to a height of three feet. The leaves are pinnately lobed, with deep indentations and sharply tipped lobes; the stem contains a bitter, orange-colored sap. Prickly poppy flowers reach a diameter of two or three inches, and

155

are borne singly or in small groups. Each flower has a regular perianth with four to six papery petals and three sepals. This poppy, found from Colorado and Texas westward, is in flower from June to August. MATILIJA POPPY is a taller plant, growing to a height of six feet and becoming a bushy mass of foliage and showy flowers. The leaves are pinnately lobed and the stems are smooth. Matilija poppies produce extremely large flowers, four or five inches in diameter. Each flower has a regular perianth of three sepals and six petals, an unusual number for a Dicot. Matilija poppies grow in the canyons and river beds of southern California.

CREAM-CUPS is another western member of the Poppy family, found in dry habitats of southern California. It is a low-growing plant rarely more than twelve inches tall, with semierect flower stalks. The leaves are linear, and borne opposite each other on the stems. Erect, usually solitary flowers, about three-quarters of an inch in diameter, have a regular perianth of three sepals and six white or cream-colored petals.

SOAP PLANT, or amole, is the only Monocot member of the white-flowering field species. It has the characteristic linear, parallel-veined leaves, and flowers with a perianth of six segments with no differentiation between sepals and petals. Soap plant has erect stems, reaching a height of four feet, with terminal panicles of white, purple-veined flowers, each about one inch in diameter, with narrow linear segments. Soap plant is an inhabitant of dry hills and plains of the Pacific coast states; western Indians used the bulbs for food, and their fiber coating to make into brushes.

Among the desert flora of the southwestern United

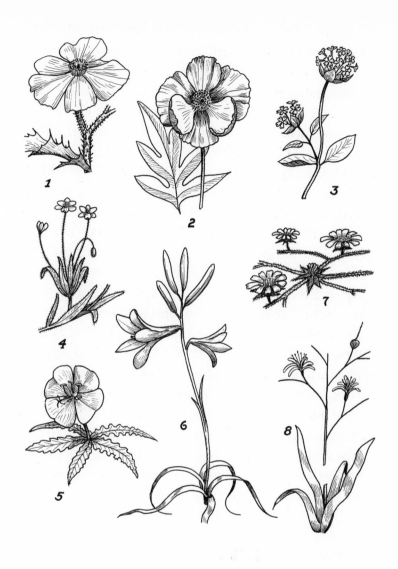

White Field Flowers of the Western United States: Prickly Poppy (1); *Matilija Poppy* (2); *Sand Verbena* (3); *Cream-cups* (4); *Desert Primrose* (5); *Desert Lily* (6); *Desert Star* (7); *Soap Plant* (8).

States are three white flowers. DESERT PRIMROSE is a low-growing plant with a basal cluster of rounded to lanceolate leaves, rarely more than one foot in length. Large regular flowers, borne in the leaf axils and reaching a diameter of several inches, have a corolla of four separate petals which are white when first open but later become pink. This primrose thrives on the sandy Colorado and Mojave Deserts of California. DESERT STAR is a prostrate, hairy composite, with linear leaves in a basal rosette from which runners extend outward in all directions, producing new plants. Daisylike flower heads, one inch broad, are borne erect on slender stems, each head with white or pinkish ray flowers and yellow disk flowers. This too is a common wild flower of the California deserts. These arid habitats seem inappropriate as the natural home of lilies; however, the DESERT LILY of Southern California and Arizona lives in this unusual environment. Narrow twisted leaves, often a foot in length, lie at the base of the plant in a coiled position. Stout stems, growing several feet tall, bear elongated racemes of flowers two inches in length. Each flower has the typical lily pattern of six similar perianth segments; in the desert lily these segments are narrow, silvery, or greenish on the outer surface, pure white on the inside.

Red and Pink Flowers

As with the white flowers, we can separate the red and pink wild flowers into three groups based on their geographic distribution. Many can be found throughout the

158

United States. These include bindweed, bouncing Bet, wild four-o'clock, spreading dogbane, and poppy mallow, all of which have regular perianths. Other widely distributed species, with irregular perianths, include Indian paint brush, fireweed, and red clover. A second group is made up of species common to the eastern United States such as rose pink and pink Cleome. The third group, found only in the western states, includes crimson sage, scarlet Gilia, groundpink, and scarlet bugler. Typical of the southwestern deserts are the red-flowered desert hollyhock, desert verbena, and desert mariposa.

BINDWEED, or wild morning glory, is a vinelike plant of dry rocky habitats and waste places; it is often found covering stone walls and fences. Bindweed is closely re-

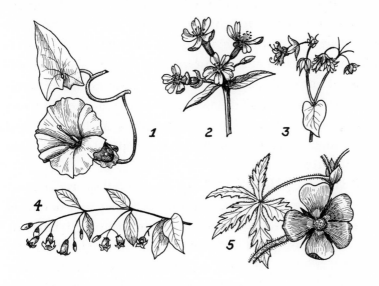

Red or Pink Field Flowers: Bindweed (1); *Bouncing Bet* (2); *Wild Four-o'clock* (3); *Spreading Dogbane* (4); *Eastern Poppy Mallow* (5).

159

lated to the cultivated morning glory and to the sweet potato. Simple triangular leaves with pointed basal lobes grow alternately on the stems. Large rosy-pink, sometimes white flowers, attaining a length of several inches, grow singly or in pairs in the leaf axils. Each flower has a calyx of five green sepals, seated above a pair of leaflike bracts. Complete fusion of the regular corolla has resulted in a vase-shaped flower with a wavy and indistinctly five-lobed margin. This common flowering vine, found from New England to the Pacific coast, is in bloom from May to September.

BOUNCING BET, a roadside wild flower that prefers cooler and damper habitats than most of its field companions, is found in all our states, flowering from July to September. A member of the Pink family, its stout branching stems, growing to a height of three feet, bear opposite oval leaves. The mucilaginous sap of bouncing Bet forms a lather with water, a feature that gives this plant the additional name of soapwort. The pink flowers, about three-quarters of an inch in diameter, are borne in spreading terminal clusters. Each flower has a cuplike and five-toothed calyx and a regular corolla of five separate petals with notched tips.

WILD FOUR-O'CLOCK, or umbrellawort, is common in the western prairie states. It grows to a height of three feet, its stems bearing opposite ovate or triangular leaves. Pink or purplish flowers are borne singly at the tips of erect stems from June to October. Like other members of the Four-o'clock family, the flowers lack a corolla; the five-lobed calyx, about three-quarters of an inch in length, is the colored portion of the perianth.

SPREADING DOGBANE, also known as mountain hemp, grows along wooded roadsides in all our states. The forking stems form bushy growths several feet in height, with oval dark-green leaves borne opposite each other. This species of dogbane often forms dense beds along the margins of woods. Dainty pink flowers, less than one-half inch in length, appear in June and continue to blossom through August; they hang like tiny bells from the horizontal branches. Each flower has a regular, urn-shaped corolla formed by fusion of the petals; the margin is edged with five recurved and pointed lobes.

EASTERN POPPY MALLOW reaches its maximum abundance on the dry plains of the central United States. It is a trailing plant with fernlike palmately lobed leaves. Red or purplish flowers, two to three inches in diameter, grow singly or in small clusters; they bloom from June through August. The regular perianth consists of five green sepals and five separate petals with squared and notched tips. As with other members of the Poppy family, the stamens of poppy mallow are fused to form a conspicuous central column surrounding the pistil. WESTERN POPPY MALLOW thrives on grassy slopes of the Pacific coast states. It is an erect plant, growing to a height of several feet, with toothed- or wavy-margined leaves. Pink or purple flowers, about one-half inch in diameter, grow in terminal racemes or spikes. Like those of its eastern relative, the petals have square tips; but in this species they are only slightly notched.

INDIAN PAINT BRUSH is also known as painted cup; both names refer to the lobed bracts beneath the flower clusters, which are tipped with bright red. Indian paint brush is an inhabitant of moist grassy slopes in the eastern United States; its erect stems, two or three feet tall, bear alternate pinnately lobed leaves and rise from a basal rosette of ovate leaves. Inconspicuous flowers, about three-quarters of an inch in length, form a dense terminal cluster amid the red bracts. Each flower has an irregular yellowish-green perianth with a two-lipped corolla; the upper lip is arched and the lower lip has three short lobes. Eastern Indian paint brush blooms from April to August. WESTREN INDIAN PAINT BRUSH adds color to the grassy hillsides of the Pacific coast. The purplish green stems, with linear leaves, grow to a height of sixteen inches. The irregular flowers, about an inch in length, are hidden among the conspicuous bright red bracts.

FIREWEED, or willow herb, is found from the Carolinas to Alaska, and from the Atlantic to the Pacific coasts. This is a welcome invader of burned-over and logged areas where it quickly moves in and conceals the ugly scars

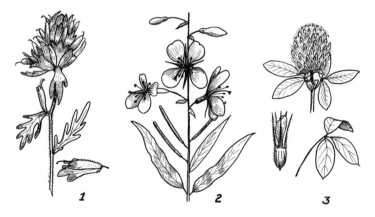

1   2   3

Red or Pink Field Flowers with Irregular Perianths: Indian Paintbrush (1); *Fireweed* (2); *Red Clover* (3).

162

brought about by human activities. Pink or purplish orchidlike flowers are borne in slender spires at the tips of erect stems five or six feet tall, bearing alternate lanceolate leaves. The showy flowers, an inch in length, are grouped in a spikelike raceme which reaches a length of twelve inches. Each flower is slightly irregular, with a calyx of four reddish lobes and a corolla of four colored petals. In autumn the inflorescence becomes transformed into a fluffy mass of wind-dispersed seeds.

RED CLOVER is a familiar and fragrant field flower which, after being introduced from Europe, has spread throughout the United States. The foliage consists of compound leaves divided into three leaflets. Minute, irregular flowers, similar in design to peas, are crowded into a compact rounded head, an inch in diameter. Other species of clover have white or purple flowers. Over a dozen species occur in the prairie states and on the Pacific coast. Clover is planted to enrich the soil, since the roots develop swellings that contain colonies of bacteria, capable of changing atmospheric nitrogen into nitrates.

ROSE PINK, or bitterbloom, has opposite ovate leaves

Red or Pink Field Flowers: Rose Pink (1) *and Pink Cleome* (2).

163

whose base clasps the square stem; other oval leaves form a basal rosette from which the erect stem arises. Rose pink, growing to a height of eighteen inches, has a spreading cluster of deep pink flowers, an inch in diameter; in some varieties the flowers are white. Each flower has a five-lobed calyx and a regular corolla of five petals with a tubular base. Rose pink is a fragrant member of the field community, in the central United States, flowering from July to September.

PINK CLEOME, or spider flower, grows in grassy fields and waste places throughout the central United States. Erect stems, three feet tall, bear alternate compound leaves divided into three narrow leaflets. The showy flowers are mingled with leafy bracts in a dense terminal raceme; they bloom from May to September. Each flower has a calyx of four sepals, united at the base, and a nearly regular corolla of four pink petals with a tubular base. Projecting beyond the corolla, which is three-quarters of an inch in diameter, is a slender stalk with stamens attached; this gives the flower a spidery appearance.

The western United States, especially California, is the home of many red or scarlet flowers. CRIMSON SAGE, a member of the Mint family, grows on moist grassy slopes. It is a coarse-stemmed plant, two or three feet in height, with opposite lanceolate leaves that are hairy and white on the underside. Crimson sage is a strongly aromatic plant, bearing whorls of flowers in a spikelike inflorescence. The irregular perianth, about an inch in length, is two-lipped; the upper lip is erect, and the spreading three-lobed lower lip is fringed in some varieties.

SCARLET GILIA, of the Phlox family, is one of fifty species of gilia found in the western United States, many of which are xerophytes of the desert wild-flower community. The foliage is often bristly and spiny. Scarlet gilia is a low-growing plant with a basal rosette of pinnately lobed, hairy leaves. Bright red flowers, about an inch in length, are borne in a terminal cluster. Each flower has a regular tubular corolla divided into five lanceolate lobes. GROUNDPINK, a close relative of scarlet gilia, is a native of California, also found in sandy dry habitats. The stems and leaves are threadlike; small flowers, about a half inch in length, are borne in small clusters. Each pink or lilac-tinted flower has a funnel-shaped calyx and a corolla with five dark spots and a yellow throat.

SCARLET BUGLER, a strongly scented bushy plant, grows commonly on gravelly slopes in southern California; it is one of nineteen western species some of which have white, yellow, or blue flowers as well as red. Many species are known as beardtongues because of the bearded stamens. Scarlet bugler is a leafy-stemmed plant growing to a height of three feet with opposite and lanceolate leaves. Each flower, one inch in length, has a calyx with five reddish lobes and a tubular two-lipped corolla. The upper lip is two-lobed, the lower lip is three-lobed; the corolla also has a distinctive dilated throat. Scarlet bugler flowers are grouped in terminal panicles that attain a length of twelve inches.

In the deserts of the southwest live two xerophytes with brilliant red flowers. DESERT HOLLYHOCK, a member of the Mallow family, inhabits canyon slopes of the Colorado and Mohave deserts. It is a bushy plant, two or three feet tall, with thick veiny leaves that are palmately lobed. Brick-red flowers grow in axillary clusters or terminal panicles. Each flower, about one inch in diameter, has a regular perianth with a five-lobed calyx and five separate petals. DESERT MARIPOSA, a member of the Lily family, is a low-growing plant, rarely more than eight inches tall, with narrow linear leaves. The regular flowers consist of three red-tinted sepals and three vermilion petals, spotted with purple at the base. The flowers grow to be an inch or more in diameter. Desert mariposa lives on the open flats and slopes of southern California and Arizona.

A memorable sight along the desert roadsides of the southwest is the colorful carpet of DESERT VERBENA, whose pink or lavender flowers are part of the wild-flower display that follows the March and April rains. It is a sprawling, low-growing plant with opposite oval leaves and flowers in terminal umbels, seated in leafy bracts. Desert verbena is a member of the Four-o'clock family,

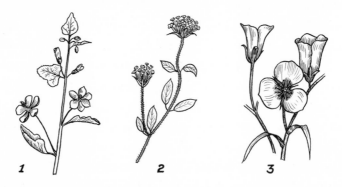

Red or Pink Field Flowers of the Western United States: Desert Hollyhock (1); *Desert Verbena* (2); *Desert Mariposa* (3).

166

and thus its flowers lack a corolla but in its place have a colored calyx. The calyx has a slender tubular base and an expanded saucerlike rim with four or five lobes.

Yellow and Orange Flowers

A great number of the xerophytic plants that colonize dry fields, roadsides, and similar sunny habitats have yellow or orange flowers. Many are composites that possess adaptations for living in such an environment. Also, in contrast with the spring-blooming woodland flowers, most of these yellow-flowering field species bloom in summer and autumn. To simplify our identification of these flowers, we will separate them according to the regions where they live, as we have done with the white and red flowers: those which are found throughout the United States, those which occur in the central and eastern states, and those which are restricted to the region west of the Rocky Mountains.

Wild flowers that are likely to be encountered anywhere in the United States include many familiar species with regular flowers such as buttercup, five-finger, sourgrass, evening primrose, and butterfly weed. This group also includes some with irregular flowers, of which butter-and-eggs and mullein are typical. A large number in the group are composites: sunflower, goldenrod, tickseed, beggar-ticks, and dandelion.

Buttercups form a large assemblage of sun-loving plants, some of which grow in dry fields and along roadsides, others in the more mesophytic habitats of moist

167

meadows and ditches. There are thirty-six different kinds of buttercup growing in the northeastern United States, over twenty in the southeastern states, and eight in the western United States. The common FIELD BUTTER-CUP, a European immigrant, grows to a height of several feet and has branching stems bearing alternate compound leaves, palmately divided into five narrow, toothed leaflets. The flowers, about one-half inch in diameter, grow singly or in small clusters; each flower has a regular perianth of five green sepals and five bright yellow petals. The shape of the leaf gives some species of buttercup the alternate name of crowfoot. Field buttercups flower from May to August. The CALIFORNIA BUTTERCUP of grassy meadows and hillsides, growing to a height of several feet, has erect branching stems and palmately three-lobed leaves. The flower is the same size as the eastern buttercup, but the corolla consists of nine or more petals. Other western buttercups have pink or yellow flowers, and are mesophytes of mountain meadows.

Some Yellow or Orange Field Flowers: Five-finger (1); *Sourgrass* (2); *Evening Primrose* (3); *Butterfly Weed* (4).

FIVE-FINGER, or cinquefoil, a member of the Rose family, is one of a large group of several dozen species. The common eastern five-finger is a prostrate plant, usually under six inches in height and spreading by runners that extend through the grasses. The palmately compound leaves are made up of five serrate leaflets, radiating outward like fingers. The flowers, about one-half inch in diameter, are borne singly or in small clusters; the regular perianth consists of five green sepals and five rounded petals. Five-finger can be found in flower from March through June. WESTERN FIVE-FINGER is a slightly more erect plant, growing to a height of two feet, with reddish foliage and palmately compound leaves with three to five leaflets. Small flowers, one-quarter inch in diameter, are borne in a spreading leafy cluster; the corolla is pale yellow or cream-colored. This five-finger prefers more shaded habitats than most species; it grows on canyon slopes of the Pacific coast.

SOUR-GRASS, or creeping sorrel, is a European immigrant with sour watery sap and prostrate stems that root at the nodes; it often becomes a weed in lawns and gardens. The compound leaves are palmately divided into three leaflets, resembling those of clover but with a notched tip. Small regular flowers, one-half inch broad or less, are borne singly or in small clusters. Each flower has five separate green sepals and five rounded petals, slightly united at the base. Sour-grass flowers during a long period, from April to November. CALIFORNIA WOOD SORREL, found on stony hillsides, has similar foliage and habits; the pale yellow or purplish flowers, however, are borne in pairs.

169

EVENING PRIMROSE, a stout-stemmed plant growing to a height of six feet, has hairy foliage and stems and alternate lanceolate leaves. It thrives in sandy soil and waste places in the eastern United States; related species live on moist slopes of the western states. There are eighteen kinds of evening primrose in the eastern states, twenty-five in the west. The flowers, reaching a diameter of one to two inches, are borne in a leafy spikelike terminal cluster; they are unusual in opening only during late afternoon and evening. Each flower has a long tubular calyx with four reflexed lobes, and a regular corolla of four large petals. Evening primroses are in flower from June to October.

BUTTERFLY WEED, or pleurisy root, a member of the Milkweed family, has the floral structure of a milkweed, with a set of hooded elevations forming a corona at the center of the corolla. Butterfly weed is a hairy-stemmed, stout plant with alternate lanceolate leaves, and grows two or three feet in height. Brilliant orange flowers are clustered in a dense terminal umbel. Each flower has a regular corolla about one-quarter inch in length, with five reflexed petals. The fruit is a silky pod, four or five inches in length. Butterfly weed grows in sunny fields and along roadsides from New England to Texas.

BUTTER-AND-EGGS, also known as wild snapdragon or yellow toadflax, is a European immigrant which has established itself in sandy waste places throughout the United States. Slender stems, two or three feet tall, bear alternate linear leaves and terminate in a spikelike raceme of bicolored flowers. Each flower, about one inch in length, has an irregular two-lipped corolla, spurred at the base.

170

The upper lip is two-lobed and erect, the lower lip is three-lobed and spreading; both lips are light yellow. The throat of the corolla, between the lips, is closed by a deep-orange projection. Below the tubular base of the corolla is a five-parted green calyx. Butter-and-eggs has a long flowering period, from May to October.

COMMON MULLEIN, or flannel plant, is another European immigrant, which thrives in such unfavorable habitats as sand and gravel banks and stony fields. It is one of the most xerophytic members of the eastern field community, suited by its woolly, feltlike leaves to grow in such locations. Large yellowish and elliptic leaves form a basal rosette from which a stout leafy stem rises to a height of six feet, terminating in a spirelike inflorescence

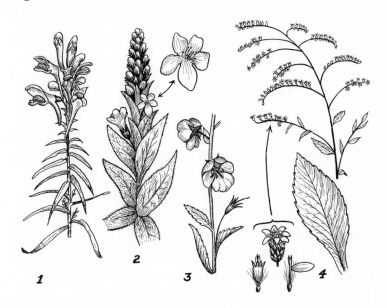

Some Yellow Field Flowers: Butter-and-eggs (1); *Common Mullein* (2); *Moth Mullein* (3); *Canada Goldenrod* (4).

171

of crowded flowers. Each pale yellow flower, about three-quarters of an inch in diameter, has a five-parted green calyx and a slightly irregular corolla of five petals; the three upper petals are smaller than the two lower ones. Common mullein can be found in flower from June to September, and occurs throughout the United States. MOTH MULLEIN, another European species found in waste places and along roadsides in all our states, is a slenderer plant with smooth stems three or four feet tall that bear alternate ovate leaves. Flowers, one inch in diameter, are clustered in a loose terminal raceme; each pale yellow flower is slightly irregular, as in common mullein.

Sunflowers make up one of the largest groups of flowers in the field community, with at least forty-three different species in the southeastern United States, twenty-five in the Northeast, and six on the Pacific coast. They are perhaps our most typical American composite. COMMON SUNFLOWER, native to the central United States, has been introduced both eastward and westward where it thrives in rich soil and sunny exposures. It is an erect tall plant, with stems growing to a height of eight feet; under a cultivation this giant among our wild flowers reaches a stature of ten feet or more. Large cordate or elliptic leaves grow alternately on the stems. The flower heads, two to six inches in diameter in the wild varieties, consist of yellow ray flowers several inches in length, and a disk equally broad of closely packed tubular brown or purple flowers. The blooming of sunflowers heralds late summer, since they are in flower from July to October. Cultivated varieties have much larger heads, and large brown achenes as fruits which yield an oil important in making soap and cattle feed. The sunflower "seeds" (achenes) were eaten by the American Indians and even today are a part of the diet of rural Eurasian peoples. WOODLAND SUNFLOWER is a smaller plant of roadside thickets in eastern United States, with opposite lanceolate leaves and stems two to seven feet tall. Flower heads about two inches in diameter are borne in branching terminal clusters.

Another large group of American wild flowers, also composites, is that which includes the goldenrods, with seventy-five species in the eastern and southern United States. Westward the goldenrods decrease in numbers, with only a half dozen species on the Pacific coast. Goldenrods are erect, branched or unbranched plants with alternate simple leaves and numerous very small flower heads, one-quarter of an inch or less in diameter; these are grouped in flat-topped or plumelike panicles, or slender rodlike spires. Each head is made up of a few ray and disk flowers seated in a cuplike involucre; both ray and disk flowers are yellow. In New England goldenrods are late summer and autumn flowers, appearing in August and continuing in bloom through October. There is hardly a field or roadside that is not brightened by the golden-yellow masses of these widely distributed companions of the asters. CANADA GOLDENROD is an attractive eastern species, growing three or four feet tall with flower heads in an arching, plumelike inflorescence; its leaves are lanceolate, with a toothed margin. GRASS-LEAVED GOLDENROD, also of the eastern United States, has narrow grasslike leaves. It is a smaller plant, usually only a few feet tall, with flower heads in flat-topped terminal clusters. WREATH GOLDENROD, more common on the sunny edges of thickets, is also a smaller and slender plant, with purplish stems and sessile lanceolate leaves. Small clusters of flower heads are borne in the axils of the leaves and in rodlike terminal racemes. CALIFORNIA GOLDENROD, common on dry hillsides, has un-branched upright stems with grayish-green elliptic leaves and flower heads in slender terminal spires.

The tickseeds, or coreopsis, are attractive composites with a number of species in both the eastern and western United States, some of which are planted as garden orna-mentals. The flower heads usually have eight conspicuous ray flowers and a disk of tubular flowers; both ray and disk flowers are yellow in most species. Each head is seated in a double row of bracts, forming a conspicuous involucre. LANCE-LEAVED TICKSEED is a slender

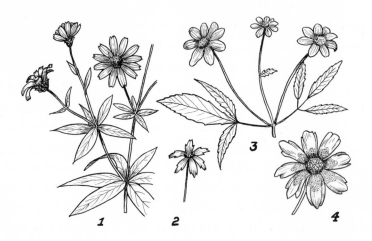

Some Yellow Composite Field Flowers: Common Tickseed (1); *Lance-leaved Tickseed* (2); *Beggar-tick* (3); *Dye-flower* (4).

174

erect plant, several feet in height, with opposite lanceolate leaves. Several flower heads, each about two inches in diameter, are borne on long slender stalks. Each head has wedge-shaped ray flowers, notched at the tip. Lance-leaved tickseed, a wild flower of dry thickets and roadsides of the southeastern United States, flowers from May to July. The name "tickseed" refers to the prickly achene fruit, which has stiff spines at the angles. COMMON TICKSEED, with flower heads one inch in diameter, is another eastern species; it grows to a height of three feet, and has sessile, palmately compound leaves. Showiest of all the species is DYE-FLOWER of the central United States, whose large heads, up to two inches in diameter, consist of yellow ray flowers with a crimson-brown base, and a disk of dark-red tubular flowers. Under the name of Calliopsis, this species is grown as a garden ornamental.

Another group of common composites includes the beggar-ticks, very similar to the tickseeds in flower characteristics and the double involucre. The annoying, prickly fruits are well known to the exploring naturalist who serves as an unwilling means of their dispersal; each fruit is an elongated achene with two or three barbed spines at its tip. The ray flowers may be yellow or white, the disk flowers are yellow; three to eight ray flowers develop in each head in most species; they may be entirely lacking in others. COMMON BEGGAR-TICKS, also known as Spanish needles and bur-marigold, is common in moist fields and thickets throughout the United States. It is a much-branched plant, one to three feet tall, with reddish-brown and furrowed stem; the leaves are compound, with three to five toothed leaflets. Small yellow flowers appear in August, continuing in bloom until October.

It seems hardly necessary to describe that most familiar of all composites, the COMMON DANDELION, which often abandons fields and waste places to invade lawns and gardens. This is a naturalized European species, found throughout the United States and flowering from early spring until late autumn. Dandelion belongs to a group of composites whose heads include ray flowers only; these form large orange-yellow inflorescences one inch or more in diameter, borne singly on short succulent stems with a milky juice. The plants are low-growing, with a compact basal rosette of elongated, pinnately lobed and sharply toothed leaves. The small achenes of dandelion are provided with tufts of hairs that enable the fruit to float through the air, an efficient means of plant dispersal.

In the field and roadside communities of the eastern United States occur many wild flowers that are rarely found west of the Rocky Mountains. Some of these have regular flowers: St.-John's-wort, yellow star-grass and Canada lily. Others have irregular flowers: partridge pea and wild indigo. And among these eastern wild flowers are such familiar composites as orange hawkweed, king devil, tansy, and black-eyed Susan.

COMMON ST.-JOHN'S-WORT, one of twenty-five species, is a coarse-stemmed and many-branched plant growing to a height of three feet. It is a European immigrant that has colonized old fields and pastures; related species live in more hydrophytic habitats of wet woods and marshes. Common St.-John's-wort has opposite linear leaves, and flowers that occur in leafy clusters at the tips of the stems. Each flower has a regular perianth, one-half

176

Yellow or Orange Field Flowers of the Eastern United States:
St.-John's-wort (1); *Yellow Star-grass* (2); *Black-eyed Susan*
(3); *Partridge Pea* (4); *Wild Indigo* (5); *Orange Hawkweed*
(6); *King Devil* (7); *Tansy* (8).

Canada lily is a wild flower of shaded fields and edges of woods, its nodding pale-yellow flowers consisting of three sepals and three petals colored alike.

to one inch in diameter, with a bright yellow corolla of five separate petals. The flowers can be found from June to September.

YELLOW STAR-GRASS, a member of the Amaryllis family, has typical Monocot grasslike leaves; it is a low-growing stemless plant of sunny fields of the eastern United States. The flower stalks bear terminal clusters of a few star-shaped regular flowers, each less than one-half inch broad. Yellow star-grass flowers have a perianth of six segments, with no differentiation between sepals and petals. They appear in spring and continue to bloom through summer. CANADA LILY is another Monocot, found in moist fields as well as in open woods. Growing to a height of four feet, this graceful lily has erect stems with lanceolate leaves in whorls of four or more; each stem often has six to ten such whorls of leaves. Pale yellow, vase-shaped flowers each several inches in length, develop singly or in small clusters at the summit of the plant. Each flower is nodding, with six similar segments that are usually recurved. Canada lily is a species of the eastern United States, flowering in June and July.

PARTRIDGE PEA, also known as golden cassia or prairie senna, is a member of the Pea family, characterized by the typical pinnately compound leaves and irregular flowers. It is a sprawling plant, growing only a foot or two in height. The compound leaves, with ten to fifteen leaflets, are sensitive to touch; related species also with this characteristic are known as wild sensitive plants. Partridge pea flowers are borne in groups of two or four in the leaf axils. Each flower, about one inch in length, has a slightly irregular corolla of five spreading petals. This wild flower thrives in sunny habitats of the eastern and central United States, where its orange-yellow flowers can be found from July to September. WILD INDIGO, or horsefly weed, another member of the Pea family, is a plant of roadsides and clearings in the woods; it is in flower from June to September. Wild indigo grows to a height of several feet, with palmately compound cloverlike leaves. Small bright yellow flowers, less than one-half inch in length, grow in terminal clusters mingled with the foliage. Each flower has an erect petal only slightly larger than the two lateral petals and the petals that form the keel of the corolla.

179

TANSY, also appropriately called golden buttons, is a European composite which has spread throughout the eastern United States and Canada. It can be recognized by the strongly aromatic and fernlike foliage. Tansy inhabits roadsides and fields where it often forms dense beds three or four feet tall, with pinnately compound leaves and flat-topped clusters of compact flower heads. Each head, less than one-half inch in diameter, consists of a few small yellow ray flowers which project only a short distance beyond the more conspicuous disk of numerous yellow tubular flowers. Tansy is in flower from August to September, contributing its golden hue to the autumn wild-flower display.

ORANGE HAWKWEED, or devil's paintbrush, is another European composite that has made itself at home in sunny fields and spread as a weed to lawns and gardens. Orange hawkweed has a basal cluster of elliptic hairy leaves from which rises a leafless flower stalk, also hairy, a foot or more in height. One to several orange-yellow flower heads, each one-half to three-quarters of an inch in diameter, terminate this stalk. Like dandelion, orange hawkweed consists of ray flowers only; each ray flower has a five-toothed margin. Orange hawkweed can be found in flower from June to August. KING DEVIL, a bright yellow hawkweed, is also a common weed throughout the eastern United States. It has the same basal rosette of leaves from which the flower stalk rises to a height of one or two feet. The flower heads, borne singly or in small clusters, are the same size as those of orange hawkweed, but are bright yellow in color. In addition to the immigrant hawkweeds, over a dozen other species are native to the United States.

BLACK-EYED SUSAN, also known as yellow cone-flower or yellow daisy, is a showy composite of sunny fields throughout the eastern United States. The stems and foliage are rough and hairy, with alternate narrow stem leaves and ovate basal leaves. Erect stems, growing two or three feet tall, bear single or several large heads, each two or three inches in diameter. Ten to twenty golden-yellow ray flowers surround a cone-shaped disk made up of dark-brown tubular flowers. Black-eyed Susan is a late summer flower, appearing in August and continuing in bloom through September. This is one of several dozen species of coneflowers found in New England and the central United States.

Yellow or orange flowers of the western United States include some, like California poppy and fiddleneck, that have regular flowers; others, like locoweed and golden eardrops, have irregular flowers; and the usual group of field composites such as desert dandelion, tarweed, goldfields, and tidy-tips. CALIFORNIA POPPY, the state flower, is one of the most conspicuous members of the colorful wild-flower display that occurs every spring on California hillsides. These poppies, one to two feet in height, have compound leaves finely dissected into very narrow lobes. Solitary erect flowers of golden yellow, an inch or two in diameter, have two sepals and a graceful cup-shaped corolla of four petals. California poppies begin blooming with the first spring rains and continue through summer. This western wild flower is grown as a garden ornamental in the eastern United States.

FIDDLENECK, or yellow forget-me-not, is a pungent and bristly plant of dry slopes and desert roadsides. About

California poppy, the state flower, adds its golden-yellow hue to the wild-flower display which every spring turns California hillsides into a sea of color.

twelve inches in height, the stems bear alternate linear or lanceolate leaves. Orange-yellow regular flowers are borne in one-sided, curved spikes; each corolla is tubular and five-lobed, about one-quarter inch in length. Fiddleneck is found throughout the southwestern United States.

LOCOWEED, a grayish-green plant, one to three feet tall, often occupies miles of dry prairies and wastelands in the western United States. "Loco" is the Spanish word for crazy, and refers to the effect the poisonous substance found in this plant has on cattle and horses. A member of the Pea family, locoweed has pinnately compound leaves and small yellowish-brown irregular flowers in elongated

182

Yellow or Orange Field Flowers of the Western United States:
Fiddleneck (1); *Locoweed* (2); *Golden Ear-drops* (3); *Desert*
Dandelion (4); *Tarweed* (5); *Gold-fields* (6); *Tidy-tips* (7).

racemes. Each flower, about one-quarter inch in length, has a five-toothed calyx and slender pealike corolla. The flowers of some species are blue, of others white or scarlet. Locoweed blooms from June to August. The effect upon animals feeding on this plant is muscular weakness, lack of appetite, incoordination, and eventually death.

GOLDEN EARDROPS is a western cousin of Dutchman's breeches. It is an erect branching plant, growing two or three feet tall, with narrowly lobed and pinnately compound leaves. Bright yellow flowers, one-half inch in length, are borne in an erect spreading panicle. Each irregular flower has two scalelike sepals and four petals. One pair of petals is large, spreading, and spurred; the other inner pair is smaller and forms a sac over the anthers and stigma. Golden eardrops flowers in spring, being found on stony river beds and hillsides of California.

TARWEED, a sticky, heavily scented plant of the western United States, is especially common in California and Oregon; it thrives along dry roadsides and in waste places. Tarweed grows to a height of several feet, with alternate linear leaves. The flower heads, each about three-quarters of an inch in diameter, are grouped in panicles. Each head consists of twelve to fifteen yellow ray flowers, with a three-lobed tip, and yellow tubular disk flowers. Tarweed flowers open in the evening and close the following morning.

DESERT DANDELION is an attractive xerophytic relative of the common eastern dandelion, found in desert and other arid habitats of southern California. It is a stemless plant with a dense rosette of slender, pinnately lobed leaves which when young are covered with woolly

184

hairs. Erect flower stalks, four to twelve inches tall, bear solitary flower heads; each head, about one inch in diameter, consists of bright yellow ray flowers only. Desert dandelion has a fragrant blossom, opening only in the sunshine.

GOLD-FIELDS has earned its appropriate common name from the dense mats in which this small composite grows, covering acres of sandy flats with golden-yellow flowers. Gold-fields is a low-growing plant, four to eight inches tall, with opposite narrow and entire leaves. Small flower heads, about one-half inch in diameter, grow in erect clusters; each head bears a dozen yellow ray flowers and a disk of tubular yellow flowers. This spring xerophyte can be found from California to Oregon.

TIDY-TIPS describes by its name the neat white border which marks the tip of each yellow ray flower. Tidy-tips is another low-growing composite, less than twelve inches tall, found in dry and sandy habitats of California. The basal leaves are oblong and toothed, the stem leaves narrower and lobed. Several showy heads, one inch or more in diameter, are borne in terminal clusters. Each head is made up of five to twelve ray flowers, with a squared and notched margin.

Blue and Purple Flowers

Some of the blue or purple flowers of fields and roadsides have a wide range, extending from the Atlantic to the Pacific seacoasts. Typical of these are one Monocot, blue-eyed grass, and numerous Dicots such as periwinkle, lupine, vetch, wild pea, heal-all, and blue vervain, as well as a large assemblage of composites. The latter include thistle, chicory, aster, and daisy fleabane.

BLUE-EYED GRASS is a tufted plant, under twelve inches in height, with grasslike leaves. This diminutive member of the Iris family lives in damp meadows and on grassy hillsides throughout the United States. Small blue or violet star-shaped flowers about one quarter-inch in breadth, are borne on stiffly erect stems. Each flower has a regular perianth of three sepals and three petals, colored alike and ending in a pointed tip. The flowers are clustered in green leaflike bracts. Blue-eyed grass is in flower from May through July.

PERIWINKLE, or myrtle, is a European garden plant which has escaped from cultivation to become a common trailing wild flower of shaded roadsides. It was brought to the United States by the early settlers along the eastern seacoast and has now spread throughout the country. The stems bear dark-green, ovate, opposite leaves; solitary flowers develop in the leaf axils. The violet-blue regular corolla, growing to a diameter of three-quarters of an inch, has a slender tubular base and an expanded saucer-like rim of five lobes; the flowers can be found from March to June. Periwinkle often forms a dense ground cover beneath shrubs and trees.

The lupines constitute a large group of American wild flowers, with the species increasing in numbers westward to the Pacific coast. The name, derived from the Latin word for "wolf," was given these plants because they were once thought to rob the soil of its minerals. Disproving this early superstition, today some species are used to en-

Blue or Purple Field Flowers: Blue-eyed Grass (1); *Periwinkle*
(2); *Lupine* (3); *Wild Pea* (4); *Cow Vetch* (5); *Blue Vervain*
(6); *Heal-all* (7); *Chicory* (8); *Daisy Fleabane* (9).

Lupine has spirelike clusters of pealike flowers which may be blue, yellow, white, or bicolored; it often covers acres of grassy slopes with an azure carpet.

rich the soil. Lupines have large, palmately compound leaves and irregular pealike flowers in showy terminal spires; being members of the Pea family, lupines have a pod as fruit. In a lupine flower the sides of the upright petal are reflexed, and the two lower petals form a sickle-shaped keel. The COMMON LUPINE of the eastern United States is a spring and early summer wild flower of sandy fields and dry clearings; it is an erect plant, growing to several feet in height, with long-petioled leaves that consist of seven to eleven leaflets. Purplish blue flowers are borne in a tapering terminal raceme, often a foot or two in length. Other species of eastern lupine have white or pink flowers. In southern woodlands, sandy openings are the home of a species with a white center to the upright petal of the otherwise blue flower. The bluebonnets of Texas, which cover grassy fields with azure every spring, are another species of lupine. Most showy species of all is WESTERN LUPINE which forms a spectacular display on the grassy slopes of California foothills. Western lupine grows two feet tall, and has a terminal inflorescence made up of whorls of deep-blue flowers with a yellow spot on each upright petal. Other species of western lupine have flowers of yellow, light blue, or white.

Cow vetch and wild pea are two additional members of the Pea family; their pinnately compound leaves end in tendrils that aid these wild flowers to climb over other plants for support. COW VETCH, or Canada pea, is a European immigrant of fields and roadsides that has also become a weed in lawns and gardens. The angular procumbent stems grow to a length of six feet; the compound leaves consist of eight to twelve pairs of leaflets. Deep-blue flowers are borne in one-sided racemes in the leaf axils, each flower only one-quarter inch in length. Cow vetch is among the dozen eastern species, with a half-dozen more in western United States. The flowers are in bloom from May through August. WILD PEA, also known as vetchling, has similar pinnately compound leaves terminating in tendrils. The flowers, however, are larger, up to three-quarters of an inch in length, and there are eight to ten in each raceme; the corolla is rose-purple. Wild pea also is found throughout the United States.

HEAL-ALL, a member of the Mint family, has the characteristic four-angled stems of the family. Introduced

189

from Europe, this sprawling wild flower with opposite ovate leaves rarely stands more than twelve inches tall. Heal-all is common in pastures, fields, and along roadsides in all our states. The inflorescence is a compact cylindrical head of small blue flowers mingled with green leafy bracts. Each flower has an irregular two-lipped perianth; the upper lip arches over the lower one, which is spreading and three-lobed. Heal-all can be found in flower from spring through summer.

BLUE VERVAIN, of the Verbena family, also has stiff four-angled stems; but in this species they are rough and hairy, and grow to a height of three feet, with pairs of ovate toothed leaves. Blue vervain has small, slightly irregular flowers in a slender cylindrical spike, six inches in length. Each flower has a tubular corolla, about one-quarter inch in length, with a five-lobed margin. Blue vervain grows in both dry and moist habitats throughout the United States, flowering from July to September.

BULL THISTLE is a colorful field composite introduced from Europe, which has become a widespread and obnoxious member of our wild-flower community. Its prickly foliage protects it from grazing animals so that it spreads rapidly in pastures. Bull thistle is a coarse plant, five or six feet tall, with alternate, narrowly lobed leaves edged with sharp teeth. Lavender or purplish flowers are borne in a compact head, seated in a spherical spiny involucre. Each head, one or two inches in diameter, consists of tubular disk flowers only, whose corollas are cleft into slender threadlike lobes. This thistle blooms during late summer, from July to September. The fruits are small achenes provided with tufts of downy hairs that enable the fruits to be air-borne for considerable distances before settling down to germinate. Bull thistle is one of several dozen kinds of thistles found in all our states.

CHICORY, a European garden flower which has escaped to join the native roadside wild flowers, is a composite which grows to a height of three feet, with oblong toothed or pinnately lobed leaves. The flower heads are sessile and clustered on sparsely leaved branches. Each head is composed of ray flowers only, which are light blue and square-tipped, forming a showy inflorescence one inch or more in diameter. Chicory roots are ground and roasted for use as an additive to coffee.

The blue- and purple-flowered asters contribute much of the color that tints eastern fields and roadsides into various shades of blue at the close of summer. The asters, whose white species we have already met, make up a large group of wild flowers, with over one hundred species in the eastern United States, and more than forty additional ones in the western states. Asters have alternate lanceolate leaves, usually ovate or cordate in shape, and many-branched stems terminating in clusters of flower heads. Each head consists of both ray and disk flowers. NEW ENGLAND ASTER is a stout, hairy-stemmed plant three to six feet tall, with flower heads an inch or more in breadth. The ray flowers, numbering forty or fifty in a head, are narrow and deep blue; the numerous tubular disk flowers are a golden yellow. This species is more mesophytic than most asters, preferring shaded banks and meadows. LATE PURPLE ASTER is another eastern species, of smaller size, with stiff slender stems and ovate leaves that clasp the stem. Solitary flower heads, one inch

191

Asters contribute blue and purple to the riot of color which paints each roadside during the New England autumn.

broad, have twenty to thirty ray flowers. This is a species of moderately dry fields and thickets. The western United States is the home of several species of blue-flowered asters, many of them growing in wet meadows high in the mountains.

DAISY FLEABANE, a slender-stemmed composite, resembles a small aster but usually grows from a basal cluster of ovate leaves and has unbranched stems two or three feet tall. One or several flower heads terminate the flower stalk, each head less than one inch in diameter, with a flattened compact appearance owing to the crowded ray flowers, which may number as many as a hundred. The ray flowers are light blue, the disk flowers are yellow. Daisy fleabane is a mesophytic field flower, in blossom from May through August. ROBIN'S PLANTAIN is a similar plant of the eastern United States, with broader heads usually consisting of no more than fifty ray flowers. It seldom grows taller than two feet and most of the foliage is in the basal rosette of hairy leaves.

Some of the blue or purple flowers are found chiefly east of the Rocky Mountains. In this group are bluet, field mallow, pasque flower, and purple milkweed—all with regular flowers; and birdfoot violet, viper's bugloss and dayflower with irregular flowers. BLUET, also known as innocence and Quaker ladies, is a low-growing tufted plant of the eastern United States and is rarely more than six inches tall; it is partial to moist grassy habitats and open woodland glades. Oblong or elliptic leaves are grouped in a basal cluster, and narrower leaves grow opposite each other on the stems. Each flower, about a quarter-inch in diameter, has a regular tubular corolla with four spreading lobes; the flower is light blue, with a yellow center. Bluets can be found in flower from early spring to the first frost.

FIELD MALLOW, a European garden plant that has escaped to fields and roadsides, is a trailing or somewhat erect plant of the eastern United States with pale blue or lilac-white flowers. The stems bear cordate lobed leaves and flowers about three-quarters of an inch in diameter. Each flower has a regular corolla of five petals, notched at the tip. The base of each petal is narrowed into a bearded, stalklike portion. Field mallow blossoms from June to September. Because of the rounded, wrinkled flat fruit, field mallow is also called cheeses.

PASQUE FLOWER is an attractive member of the Buttercup family, related to the anemones; it is common in the grassland communities of the central United States, extending its range as far north as the Arctic. Pasque

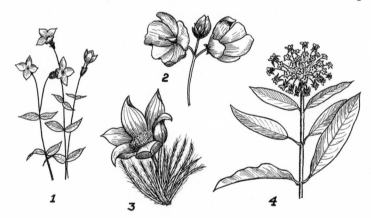

Blue or Purple Field Flowers: Bluet (1); *Field Mallow* (2); *Pasque Flower* (3); *Purple Milkweed* (4).

194

flower is a silky-hairy plant, usually less than twelve inches in height, with a basal crown of compound leaves with linear grasslike lobes. Large erect and solitary flowers appear in spring, from April to June. Pasque flowers have a regular perianth, one or two inches broad, made up of five to seven broad sepals, colored lilac-purple or white; there is no corolla, as is the case with many of the Buttercup family we have already met. In the center of the colored calyx is a mass of golden-yellow stamens.

PURPLE MILKWEED, or common milkweed, is a rank-growing plant of eastern fields and roadside thickets, growing five or six feet tall; it can be found in flower from June to August. This milkweed has oval or lanceolate leaves in pairs, and small fragrant flowers in dense terminal umbels. The regular flowers have a corolla of five petals, with a central corona of hooded projections. Milkweed seeds are wind-dispersed by means of a tuft of silky hairs that act as a parachute; the seeds develop in elongated pods. Pods and shoots of milkweed can be cooked and eaten as a green vegetable.

BIRDFOOT VIOLET is one of our largest and most attractive violets, an inhabitant of sunny sandy habitats in open woods and fields of the eastern United States. It is a stemless species, with large acutely lobed leaves whose shape resembles a bird's footprint. The erect flower stalks bear solitary flowers that reach a diameter of one inch. The irregular spurred corolla has dark-blue upper petals, lighter-blue lower ones. Orange-tipped stamens add contrast to the center of the corolla. Birdfoot violet can be found in flower from March through June.

VIPER'S BUGLOSS, or blueweed, is a rough bristly

plant introduced from Europe, which has become a road-side weed and field flower in the eastern United States. Spotted stems grow two or three feet tall, with alternate lanceolate leaves. Conspicuous irregular flowers, pink when in bud but bright blue when mature, are borne in long terminal spikes. Each flower, about one-half inch in length, has a perianth of five sepals and a tubular corolla with inflated throat and five unequal lobes. Five reddish stamens project beyond the corolla. Viper's bugloss is in flower from June to September.

DAYFLOWER, so called because the flowers last for only a short time, is one of the few Monocots of roadsides and fields; it is also one of the few emigrants from Asia to have joined our wild-flower communities. Dayflower is a sprawling plant, reaching three feet in length, with jointed stems which root at the nodes, and with dark-green lanceolate leaves. The perianth consists of three sepals and three petals, two of which are large and violet

Blue or Purple Field Flowers with Irregular Perianths: Birdfoot Violet (1); *Viper's Bugloss* (2); *Dayflower* (3).

blue and the third is small and pale white. The flowers, about three-quarters of an inch in diameter, are clustered above a leafy green bract. Dayflower, established in damp fields and roadside ditches of the eastern United States, is in bloom from June to October.

A few additional blue or purple flowers are found only west of the Rocky Mountains; these include farewell-to-spring, owl's-clover, mariposa lily, and—in the deserts of the Southwest—squaw cabbage and desert aster. FARE-WELL-TO-SPRING, a member of the Evening Primrose family, grows on the grassy slopes and wooded hillsides

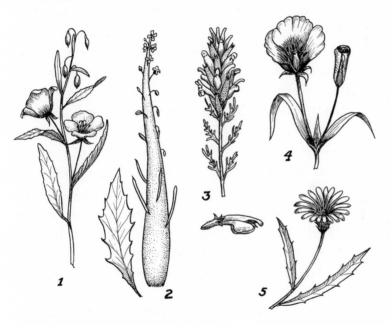

Blue or Purple Field Flowers of the Western United States: Farewell-to-spring (1); Squaw Cabbage (2); Owl's Clover (3); Mariposa Lily (4); Desert Aster (5).

197

of California; it is one of seven related species found in the western United States. Erect stems, six to twelve inches tall, bear alternate linear leaves and spikes of lavender flowers. Each flower, about one-half inch in length, has a green tubular calyx with four reflexed segments and four petals, entire or lobed. Farewell-to-spring, as its name indicates, is a late spring flower; other species have white or purple flowers.

OWL'S-CLOVER is one of the wild flowers that contributes to the mass spring flower shows of the California hillsides. It is a low-growing, bushy plant six to twelve inches tall, with alternate leaves that are sessile and deeply lobed. The upper leaves become purple bracts of the flower spike, mingling with the small irregular and two-lipped flowers. The upper lip is narrow and yellow; the lower lip, inflated to form a small white sac, is marked with purple spots and resembles the face of an owl.

SQUAW CABBAGE, also called desert candle, is an unusual member of the Mustard family which has joined the xerophytic community found on deserts of southern California. Squaw cabbage has inflated hollow stems that grow several feet tall, above a cluster of oblong basal leaves. At the leafless tip of the tapering stem small regular flowers develop, only one-quarter inch in length, with four purple sepals and four narrow white petals. When in fruit, the succulent stem bears long, upward-curving pods.

MARIPOSA LILY is a multicolored wild flower of the dry mountain slopes of California. "Mariposa" is the Spanish term for butterfly, and is aptly applied to these gaily colored flowers. Mariposa lilies grow a foot or two in

198

height, with basal grasslike leaves typical of Monocots. The solitary erect flower consists of three narrow purplish sepals and three broad lilac-blue petals with a yellow base, spotted with purple. The entire perianth resembles a delicately tinted cup.

DESERT ASTER is a hairy plant with a somewhat woody base, growing to a height of several feet; the foliage consists of pinnately lobed lanceolate leaves edged with sharp teeth. This desert composite, a close relative of the ordinary field and roadside asters, has showy heads an inch or more in diameter, with violet or lavender ray flowers and yellow disk flowers. It lives on stony slopes of the California deserts, ranging westward into Utah.

The Cacti

The Cactus family, with over two hundred American species, includes the most highly specialized of all xerophytes. Most cacti live in hot dry climates, thriving in sandy and rocky habitats. They are most abundant in the southwestern United States, from Texas to California. Many species, however, can be found in the prairie states, northward to Wyoming and Kansas. Others live amid the mesophytic vegetation of the southeastern United States, and a few hardy species have found their way up the Atlantic coast to Connecticut. Many cacti, surprisingly, can stand subfreezing temperatures and being blanketed with snow.

Cacti are, with few exceptions, leafless plants. The stems have become adapted to carry on the functions usu-

199

ally assumed by leaves, thus reducing transpiration to a minimum. The enlarged stem is green, in some species flattened and in others cylindrical or hemispherical. Because of its compact shape, the stem exposes as little surface as possible to water loss through evaporation. Many cacti are 98 per cent water, a condition resulting from effective penetrating root systems that can absorb what little moisture is present in the soil. Most cacti are armed with spines that form a thorny armor around the stems, thus aiding the plants to survive in regions where herbivorous animals would otherwise find the succulent stems a prized food. Cacti, in spite of their repulsive and grotesque appearance, have surprisingly exquisite flowers which add color and beauty to an otherwise harsh landscape. Cactus flowers consist of numerous sepals and petals, forming a cup-shaped or funnel-shaped regular perianth, often of large size and in a variety of colors. Most of the flowers bloom for but a day, and some, like the night-blooming cereus, bloom only at night.

Cacti can be divided into two groups based on their stem characteristics. One group has jointed stems, the joints being either round flat pads or cylindrical segments; typical of these are the numerous species of prickly pear, cane cactus, and cholla. The other group has cylindrical or hemispherical unjointed stems, marked by tubercles or lengthwise ridges; in this group are the pincushion cacti, the hedgehog cacti, and the barrel cacti.

Prickly pear cacti, of which there are thirty or more species in the eastern and central United States and over two dozen in the western United States, form creeping spiny plants amid grasses and shrubs, or erect branching

200

Prickly pear cactus adorns its spiny pads with large yellow blossoms after spring rains come to the desert.

plants on stony and gravelly hillsides. The stems are made up of a series of flattened pads covered with clusters of spines. Prickly pears are difficult to eradicate from fields or pastures because the pads separate readily and each one can take root and become a new plant. ATLANTIC PRICKLY PEAR has yellow flowers, several inches in diameter, with a corolla of eight to ten large petals and a central mass of numerous stamens. Its habitat ranges from the sand dunes of Florida to the rocky ridges in southern New England; the flowers appear in spring and early summer. A spineless species, known as Indian fig, has blue-green pads and juicy edible fruits called tunas, a staple item in the diet of Mexicans and Indians. Indian figs grow to a height of eight to ten feet. WESTERN PRICKLY PEARS include numerous species, usually with yellow flowers; they are common in grasslands, sagebrush plains, and on rocky hillsides. BEAVERTAIL CACTUS, a southwestern species, has spineless lavender-tinted pads that are covered with clusters of small bristly hairs. The rose-purple flowers reach a diameter of three inches.

CANE CACTUS is a shrubby species with elongated cylindrical joints instead of flattened pads. The stems, less than an inch in diameter, branch profusely to form a thorny tangle of interlocking stems three feet or more in height. The yellow flowers, about one-half inch in diameter, are smaller than those of prickly pear. Cane cactus grows in or near the intermittent stream beds of the southwestern United States. A relative known as CHOLLA, or teddy-bear cactus, is a larger cactus with a blackened main stem and a tangle of deceptively beautiful golden-yellow branches. This color is in the straw-colored sheaths of the closely packed, sharp spines. The terminal joints break off readily and stick tenaciously to the careless passer-by who carries the portion of the cholla to a new location. The flowers of this and related species are yellow, pink, or lavender.

Smallest of the unjointed species are the pincushion cacti and their relatives. These have short cylindrical stems covered with tubercles and spreading clusters of short spines. The plants grow in small clumps, or form large pincushionlike mounds of dozens of individuals. MISSOURI PINCUSHION CACTUS is a low-growing species, a few inches tall, with greenish-yellow flowers, found in the prairie states. FISHHOOK CACTUS has

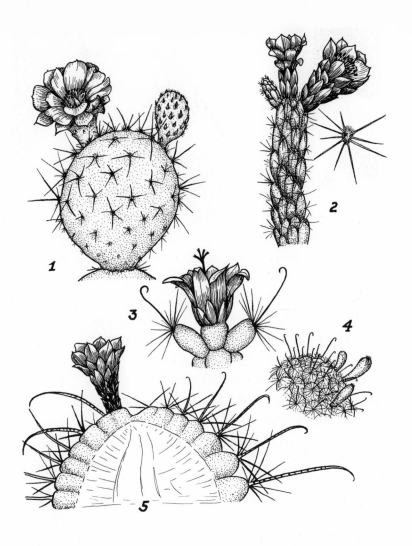

The Cacti: Prickly Pear (1); *Cholla* (2); *Fishhook Cactus flower* (3) *and fruit* (4); *Barrel Cactus* (5) *section showing watery and pulpy interior.*

Hedgehog cactus produces vase-shaped magenta flowers which are often larger than the spiny body of the plant itself.

stubby cylindrical stems, an inch or two in diameter and rarely more than six inches tall. From each cluster of spines arises a long central spine with a fishhook tip. Rose-colored or lavender flowers, an inch in diameter, grow in a circle around the stem. Pincushion cacti are favorites for indoor cactus gardens because of their small size, gregarious habit, and attractive flowers. They are native to rocky slopes from Texas to California, north to Canada.

Slightly larger in size are the hedgehog cacti, which can be recognized by the arrangement of the tubercles in lengthwise rows or ridges. The stems are a few inches in diameter and grow to a height of twelve inches. The long spines are colored red, yellow, and brown. HEDGEHOG CACTUS of the Southwest has magenta or purple flowers, several inches in diameter, which develop around the apex of the stem. The flowers appear, as do those of most cacti, in March and April; they close at night and open by day. The bright red, spineless fruit is responsible for the name STRAWBERRY CACTUS given to some species. These fruits are eaten by desert birds and reptiles. A related species, RAINBOW CACTUS, has unique clusters of radial spines, flattened and resembling small combs, set in rows so that they cover the entire surface of the stem.

Largest of all the cacti that grow amid the wild flowers of the desert community are the barrel cacti. BARREL CACTUS reaches a maximum diameter of a foot or two, and a height of ten feet; the longitudinal ribs are armed with long spines banded red and yellow. Yellow flowers, several inches in diameter, usually form a crown at the top of the barrel-like stem. This is a cactus of rocky and gravelly slopes, formerly abundant near the desert in southern California, but almost exterminated in its original home by ruthless transplanting to city homes. The treelike SAGUARO of Arizona, whose candelabralike branches reach heights of twenty and thirty feet, is also a member of this group of unjointed cacti.

We have now completed a long trek from the extreme of hydrophytic communities in ponds and swamps to the opposite extreme of the xerophytic communities of the desert. In our explorations to visit the homes of wild flowers, we have traveled from the Atlantic to the Pacific coasts. In so doing we have learned to recognize the fundamental differences and similarities existing among the members of the wild-flower communities. Among these wild flowers you have undoubtedly become reacquainted with many old friends, especially in the part of the country where you live. But you have also extended your familiarity with American wildlife by meeting many flowers that

205

you have never seen or heard of. All this should give you a more complete picture of the diversity of our wild-flower population and their varied adaptations to the many different environments that exist in our country.

HOW TO IDENTIFY SOME WHITE FIELD FLOWERS

Clue No. 1. How are the flowers arranged on the plant?

If in heads of the composite type, go to Clue No. 14.
If not in composite heads, go to Clue No. 2.

Clue No. 2. What type of symmetry does the perianth have?

If irregular, flowers in axillary clusters .... HORSEMINT.
If regular, go to Clue No. 3.

Clue No. 3. What is the nature of the perianth?

If tubular, with no free segments .... THORN APPLE.
If of separate segments (petals or sepals), go to Clue No. 4.

Clue No. 4. What is the number of the colored segments of perianth?

If in threes or sixes, go to Clue No. 5 (western U. S. only)
If in fours or fives, go to Clue No. 9.

Clue No. 5. Does the perianth have differentiated sepals and petals?

If perianth has six segments, petals and sepals alike, go to Clue No. 6.
If perianth has green sepals, colored petals, go to Clue No. 7.

Clue No. 6. How large are the flowers?

If two inches or more in length, in open raceme . DESERT LILY.
If less than one inch, in a spreading panicle ..... SOAP PLANT.

Clue No. 7. How large is the plant?

If low-growing, rarely a foot in height .... CREAM CUPS.
If erect, often bushy, over a foot in height, go to Clue No. 8.

Clue No. 8. What is the nature of the foliage?

If spiny .... PRICKLY POPPY.
If smooth .... MATILIJA POPPY.

206

Clue No. 9. How large is the flower?

    If two inches or more in diameter (western U. S.) ....
.... DESERT PRIMROSE.

    If one inch or less in diameter, go to Clue No. 10.

Clue No. 10. How are the flowers arranged on the plant?

    If solitary or in small clusters, go to Clue No. 11.

    If in axillary clusters .... SAND VERBENA.

    If in terminal umbels .... QUEEN ANNE'S LACE.

Clue No. 11. What is the nature of the calyx?

    If inflated and bladderlike .... BLADDER CAMPION.

    If not inflated, go to Clue No. 12.

Clue No. 12. What is the shape of the petals?

    If the petals are notched or cleft at the tip ..... CHICKWEED.

    If the petals are entire at the tip, go to Clue No. 13.

Clue No. 13. What is the type of leaf?

    If the leaves are compound .... WILD STRAWBERRY.

    If the leaves are simple .... SANDWORT.

Clue No. 14. What is the habit of the plant?

    If low-growing, trailing (western U. S. only) .. DESERT STAR.

    If erect, go to Clue No. 15.

Clue No. 15. What is the color of the foliage?

    If woolly white, with white involucres . PEARLY EVERLASTING.

    If not white, without white involucres, go to Clue No. 16.

Clue No. 16. What is the type of leaf?

    If compound and fernlike .... YARROW.

    If simple, go to Clue No. 17.

Clue No. 17. How large are the flower heads?

    If less than a quarter inch in diameter .... SILVERROD.

    If more than a quarter inch diameter, go to Clue No. 18.

Clue No. 18. What is the nature of the leaf margin?

    If toothed or pinnately lobed .... WHITE DAISY.

    If entire, go to Clue No. 19.

Clue No. 19. How large are the flower heads?

    If usually over half an inch in diameter .... WHITE ASTER.

    If usually less than half an inch in diameter .. CALICO ASTER.

HOW TO IDENTIFY SOME RED OR PINK FIELD FLOWERS

Clue No. 1. What type of symmetry does the perianth have?

If it is regular, go to Clue No. 2.
If it is irregular, go to Clue No. 13.

Clue No. 2. Are the colored perianth parts separate or fused?

If separate, go to Clue No. 3.
If fused to form a tubular flower, go to Clue No. 8.

Clue No. 3. What is the number of the perianth segments?

If three sepals, three colored petals (western U. S. only) .....
.... DESERT MARIPOSA.
If four sepals, four colored petals .... PINK CLEOME.
If five sepals, five petals, go to Clue No. 4.

Clue No. 4. What is the type of stem?

If it is square .... ROSE PINK.
If it is round, go to Clue No. 5.

Clue No. 5. What is the nature of the calyx?

If it is inflated and bulbous .... BOUNCING BET.
If it is not, go to Clue No. 6.

Clue No. 6. What is the shape of the petals?

If the tips are rounded, petals brick red . DESERT HOLLYHOCK.
If the tips are squared or notched, go to Clue No. 7.

Clue No. 7. What is the habit of the plant?

If trailing (eastern U. S.) .... EASTERN POPPY MALLOW.
If erect (western U. S.) .... WESTERN POPPY MALLOW.

Clue No. 8. How large is the flower?

If less than a half inch in diameter, go to Clue No. 9.
If more than a half inch in diameter, go to Clue No. 10.

Clue No. 9. How are the flowers arranged on the plant?

In umbels, plant low-growing (western U. S. only) ....
.... DESERT VERBENA.
In loose clusters; bushy plant (eastern U. S.) ....
.... SPREADING DOGBANE.

Clue No. 10. What is the shape of the flower?

If funnel-shaped, petals completely fused .... BINDWEED.
If tubular base, segments free at margin, go to Clue No. 11.

Clue No. 11. How are the flowers arranged on the plant?
If solitary or in small clusters, colored calyx, no corolla ......
.... WILD FOUR-O'CLOCK.
If in larger clusters, corolla present, go to Clue No. 12.

Clue No. 12. What is the foliage like?
If alternate, pinnate leaves .... SCARLET GILIA.
If opposite, threadlike and entire leaves .... GROUNDPINK.

Clue No. 13. Are accessory colored bracts present?
If present, adding color to the flowers ... INDIAN PAINTBRUSH.
If absent, go to Clue No. 14.

Clue No. 14. What is the nature of the corolla?
If only slightly irregular, not two-lipped .... FIREWEED.
If two-lipped, go to Clue No. 15.

Clue No. 15. What is the foliage like?
If leaves are compound, flowers in compact head. RED CLOVER.
If leaves are simple, flowers whorled or in panicles, go to Clue No. 16.

Clue No. 16. What is the nature of the corolla?
If upper lip is three-lobed, flowers in whorls ... CRIMSON SAGE.
If upper lip is two-lobed, flowers in panicles . SCARLET BUGLER.

HOW TO IDENTIFY SOME YELLOW AND ORANGE FIELD FLOWERS

Clue No. 1. How are the flowers arranged on the plant?
If they are solitary or in irregular clusters, go to Clue No. 2.
If they are in a definite type of inflorescence, go to Clue No. 8.

Clue No. 2. How many colored perianth segments are there?
If four petals, go to Clue No. 3.
If five petals, go to Clue No. 4.
If six colored segments, sepals and petals colored alike, go to Clue No. 7.

Clue No. 3. What is the color of the flowers?

If orange-yellow, leaves finely lobed .... CALIFORNIA POPPY.

If light yellow, leaves entire .... EVENING PRIMROSE.

Clue No. 4. What type of symmetry does the perianth have?

If regular, go to Clue No. 5.

If irregular .... PARTRIDGE PEA.

Clue No. 5. What is the general habit of the plant?

If erect, several feet in height .... BUTTERCUP.

If low-growing, prostrate, under a foot tall, go to Clue No. 6.

Clue No. 6. What is the type of leaf?

If compound, with three leaflets .... SOUR-GRASS.

If compound, with five leaflets .... FIVE-FINGER.

Clue No. 7. How tall is the plant?

If stemless, less than six inches tall ...... YELLOW STAR-GRASS.

If erect stems, up to four feet tall .... CANADA LILY.

Clue No. 8. What is the type of inflorescence?

If it is a head of the composite type, go to Clue No. 16.

If it is not a head, go to Clue No. 9.

Clue No. 9. What type of symmetry does the perianth have?

If it is regular, go to Clue No. 10.

If it is irregular, go to Clue No. 12.

Clue No. 10. What is the type of inflorescence?

If a one-sided, curved spike (western U. S. only) FIDDLENECK.

If not in a spike, go to Clue No. 11.

Clue No. 11. What is the nature of the corolla?

If the petals have accessory hooded structures ....
.... BUTTERFLY-WEED.

If the petals do not have such structures .. ST.-JOHN'S-WORT.

Clue No. 12. What is the nature of the corolla?

If it is irregular but not two-lipped .... MULLEIN.

If it is two-lipped, go to Clue No. 13.

Clue No. 13. What is the type of leaf?

If the leaves are simple .... BUTTER-AND-EGGS.

If the leaves are compound, go to Clue No. 14.

Clue No. 14. How are the leaflets arranged?

If the leaves are palmately compound .... WILD INDIGO.

If the leaves are pinnately compound, go to Clue No. 15.

Clue No. 15. How many petals in the corolla?

If four, flowers in spreading panicles ..... GOLDEN EARDROPS.

If five, flowers in racemes or spikes .... LOCOWEED.

Clue No. 16. How large are the flower heads?

If one-quarter inch or less in diameter .... GOLDENROD.

If more than a quarter inch in diameter, go to Clue No. 17.

Clue No. 17. What types of flowers are found in the head?

If ray flowers only are present, go to Clue No. 18.

If ray and disk flowers both are present, ray flowers large, go to Clue No. 20.

If ray flowers are inconspicuous, heads buttonlike .... TANSY.

Clue No. 18. What is the color of the ray flower?

If orange .... ORANGE HAWKWEED.

If yellow, go to Clue No. 19.

Clue No. 19. What is the nature of the stems?

If stems and leaves are hairy, entire .... KING DEVIL.

If stems and leaves are smooth, leaves pinnately lobed ....
.... DANDELION.

Clue No. 20. What is the shape of the disk?

If conical and dark brown .... BLACK-EYED SUSAN.

If flattened and saucer-shaped, go to Clue No. 21.

Clue No. 21. What is the shape of the ray flowers?

If margin of ray flowers is lobed, go to Clue No. 22.

If margin of ray flowers is entire, go to Clue No. 24.

Clue No. 22. What is the foliage like?

If sticky, heavily scented (western U.S.) .... TARWEED.

If not sticky, go to Clue No. 23.

Clue No. 23. What is the color of the ray flowers?

If entirely yellow .... TICKSEED.

If yellow with brown base .... DYE-FLOWER.

If yellow with white tips .... TIDY-TIPS.

Clue No. 24. What is the size of the flower head?

If an inch or less; go to Clue No. 25.

If more than an inch; with numerous ray flowers ....
.... SUNFLOWER.

Clue No. 25. What is the type of leaf?

If compound .... BEGGAR-TICKS.

If simple (western U. S. only) .... GOLD-FIELDS.

HOW TO IDENTIFY SOME BLUE AND PURPLE FIELD FLOWERS

Clue No. 1. How are the flowers arranged on the plant?

If in heads of the composite type, go to Clue No. 19.
If not in heads of this type, go to Clue No. 2.

Clue No. 2. What type of symmetry does the perianth have?

If regular, go to Clue No. 3.
If irregular, go to Clue No. 11.

Clue No. 3. How many segments are there in the corolla?

If four or five, go to Clue No. 4. (Dicots).
If three or six, go to Clue No. 10. (Monocots).

Clue No. 4. How large are the flowers?

If a half inch or less in diameter, go to Clue No. 5.
If more than a half inch in diameter, go to Clue No. 7.

Clue No. 5. How are the flowers arranged on the plant?

If solitary, plants less than six inches tall .... BLUET.
If clustered, plants more than six inches tall, go to Clue No. 6.

Clue No. 6. What is the type of inflorescence?

If it is a terminal umbel .... MILKWEED.
If flowers are on an erect inflated stem (California only) ....
.... SQUAW CABBAGE.

Clue No. 7. What type of leaves does the plant have?

If compound .... PASQUE FLOWER.
If simple, go to Clue No. 8.

Clue No. 8. Is the corolla of separate or fused petals?

If corolla is tubular, with five-lobed margin .... PERIWINKLE.
If the corolla is not tubular, petals separate, go to Clue No. 9.

Clue No. 9. How many petals are there?

If five, pale blue (eastern U.S.) .... FIELD MALLOW.

If four, lavender (western U.S.) ..... FAREWELL-TO-SPRING.

Clue No. 10. How large is the perianth?

If a half inch or less, deep blue, sepals and petals alike ....
.... BLUE-EYED GRASS.

If an inch or more, lilac petals, green sepals ... MARIPOSA LILY.

Clue No. 11. How many petals in the corolla?

If three (Monocot type of flower) .... DAYFLOWER.

If four or five (Dicot type of flower), go to Clue No. 12.

Clue No. 12. How are the flowers arranged on the plant?

If solitary .... BIRDFOOT VIOLET.

If in an inflorescence, go to Clue No. 13.

Clue No. 13. Do the leaves have tendrils at their tips?

If tendrils are present, go to Clue No. 14.

If tendrils are absent, go to Clue No. 15.

Clue No. 14. How large are the flowers?

If less than a half inch long .... COW VETCH.

If more than a half inch long .... WILD PEA.

Clue No. 15. What type of leaves does the plant have?

If simple, go to Clue No. 16.

If compound .... LUPINE.

Clue No. 16. Are the leaves alternate or opposite?

If alternate, go to Clue No. 17.

If opposite, go to Clue No. 18.

Clue No. 17. Does the inflorescence have accessory colored bracts?

If it does (western U.S. only) .... OWL'S GLOVER.

If it does not, foliage bristly, plant tall ...... VIPER'S BUGLOSS.

Clue No. 18. What is the nature of the corolla?

If it is two-lipped, flowers in compact spike ...... HEAL-ALL.

If irregularly lobed, flowers in elongated spike . BLUE VERVAIN.

Clue No. 19. What is the nature of the foliage?

If it is bristly and spiny .... BULL THISTLE.

If it is smooth, go to Clue No. 20.

Clue No. 20. What types of flowers occur in the head?

> *If ray flowers only* .... CHICORY.
> *If ray and disk flowers are both present, go to Clue No. 21.*

Clue No. 21. How are the leaves arranged on the plant?

> *If chiefly in basal rosette, go to Clue No. 22.*
> *If basal and on leafy stems* .... ASTER.

Clue No. 22. How many ray flowers are there?

> *If 50 or less, plant low-growing* .... ROBIN'S PLANTAIN.
> *If 50 to 100, plant taller* .... DAISY FLEABANE.

AFTERWORD

This has been only an introduction to the wild flowers of the United States. It has, I hope, whetted your appetite so that you want to learn more about the species in your own home region, as well as those you may meet in your travels. The number of books on wild flowers is almost endless, but I have selected a few which will make a valuable addition to your nature library.

Field guides, essential for identification of the species as you encounter them, are numerous; some cover large regions of the United States, some are more local and specialize on the flora of a state or portion of a state. For your nature shelf you may, however, want larger books with a greater supply of information about habitats, living habits, and other pertinent information apart from simple identification. *The Macmillan Wild Flower Book,* by Clarence

J. Hylander and Edith Farrington Johnson, describes some five hundred wild flowers found east of the Rocky Mountains; over two hundred water-color illustrations adequately present these flowers in their lifelike colors. This was published in 1954 by The Macmillan Company, New York 11, N.Y. Also published by The Macmillan Company is the invaluable *Wild Flowers* by Homer D. House (1961), describing four hundred wild flowers of the northeastern United States, illustrated by incomparable color photographs. Another publication of The Macmillan Company, *The World of Plant Life* by Clarence J. Hylander (1959), includes a great deal of information on wild flowers of the United States, especially useful in chapters on aquatic plants, saprophytes, parasites, insectivorous plants, and cacti. For the serious-minded young botanist, *Gray's Manual of Botany,* eighth edition (1950), becomes a necessity. It deals scientifically with the classification and identification of all the several thousand flowering plants of the northeastern United States and Canada. It is published by the American Book Company of Boston and New York.

If your interest is in plants of the southern or western United States, there are other books that are of value. For Southern California, *California Spring Wildflowers* by Philip A. Munz is an excellent new field guide; it is published (1961) by the University of California Press, Berkeley, California. Dr. Munz also has a more complete reference book, *A Manual of Southern California Botany,* which treats in scientific detail all the species of the southwestern United States; it is published by J. W. Stacey, Distributor, San Francisco, California. A brief but well illustrated book on the cacti is *The Cacti of Arizona* by Lyman Benson (1950), published by the University of Arizona Press, Tucson, Arizona. To enrich your knowledge of the ecological aspects of plant life, *Reading the Landscape* by May T. Watts is an entertaining story of the relation of plants (including wild flowers) to their changing environment. This was published by The Macmillan Company, New York, in 1957.

INDEX

Every kind of plant has a scientific name as well as a common one. The advantage of the scientific name is that there is only one for each kind of plant, and each plant has only one such name. Common names vary from state to state, and often the same flower has several different names in the same region. In using flower guides and books that deal with flowers scientifically, one must be familiar with the scientific names to know exactly the kind of plant one is discussing.

Each species of plant and animal has a double scientific name, indicating both the species and the genus to which it belongs. The wood lily, for example, is *Lilium philadelphicum,* with the name of the genus first and of the species second, as if we said ,"Smith, William." The genus name refers to a group of flowers with closely related traits, in this case, lilies. Another kind of lily is the Turk's-cap lily; its scientific name is *Lilium superbum;* thus it has the same genus name, but a different species name. A group of related genera (the plural of genus) is known as a family. Thus the Lily family includes not only the genus *Lilium,* but also other genera with lilylike features such as trillium (*Trillium*) and False Solomon's Seal (*Smilicina*).

217

The following is an alphabetical list of the families of wild flowers included in this book, with their genera and species.

I. THE MONOCOT WILD FLOWERS

218

IRIS FAMILY. *Iridaceae.*

LILY FAMILY. *Liliaceae.*

II. THE DICOT WILD FLOWERS

DOGBANE FAMILY. *Apocynaceae.*

224

FOUR-O'CLOCK FAMILY. *Nyctaginaceae.*

FUMITORY FAMILY. *Fumariaceae.*

GENTIAN FAMILY. *Gentianaceae.*

GERANIUM FAMILY. *Geraniaceae.*

HEATH FAMILY. *Ericaceae.*

226

MINT FAMILY. *Labiatae.*

Crimson Sage	*Salvia spathacea*	164
Heal-All	*Prunella vulgaris*	189
Hooded Skullcap	*Scutellaria epilobiifolia*	82
Horsemint	*Monarda pectinata*	154
Lyre-Leaved Sage	*Salvia lyrata*	128
Oswego Tea	*Monarda didyma*	77
Wild Mint	*Mentha canadensis*	78

MORNING GLORY FAMILY. *Convolvulaceae.*

Bindweed	*Convolvulus sepium*	159

MUSTARD FAMILY. *Cruciferae.*

Squaw Cabbage	*Caulanthus inflatus*	198

NIGHTSHADE FAMILY. *Solanaceae.*

Thorn Apple	*Datura Stramonium*	150

OXALIS FAMILY. *Oxalidaceae.*

Sour-Grass	*Oxalis corniculata*	169

PEA FAMILY. *Leguminosae.*

Clover, Red	*Trifolium pratense*	163
Cow Vetch	*Viccia cracca*	189
Locoweed	*Astragalus leucopsis*	182
Lupine, Eastern	*Lupinus perennis*	188
———, Western	——— *succulentus*	189
Partridge Pea	*Cassia fasciculata*	179

227

228

Clarence J. Hylander–*a short biography*

C. J. Hylander has had a varied career in education and research. After receiving his Ph.D. in Botany from Yale, he taught for seven years at a private country day school, at Colgate University, Hamilton, New York, and at Bowdoin College, Brunswick, Maine. He was an officer in the United States Naval Reserve during World War II, engaged in revising training manuals for Naval aviators. For several years he was executive director of the American Institute of Biological Sciences in Washington, D.C.

Dr. Hylander has made many transcontinental trips, exploring all the national parks and gaining first-hand information about the plants and animals found in the United States and taking many excellent photographs with which he illustrates his books.

He lives year-round at Bar Harbor, Maine, where he devotes full time to writing.